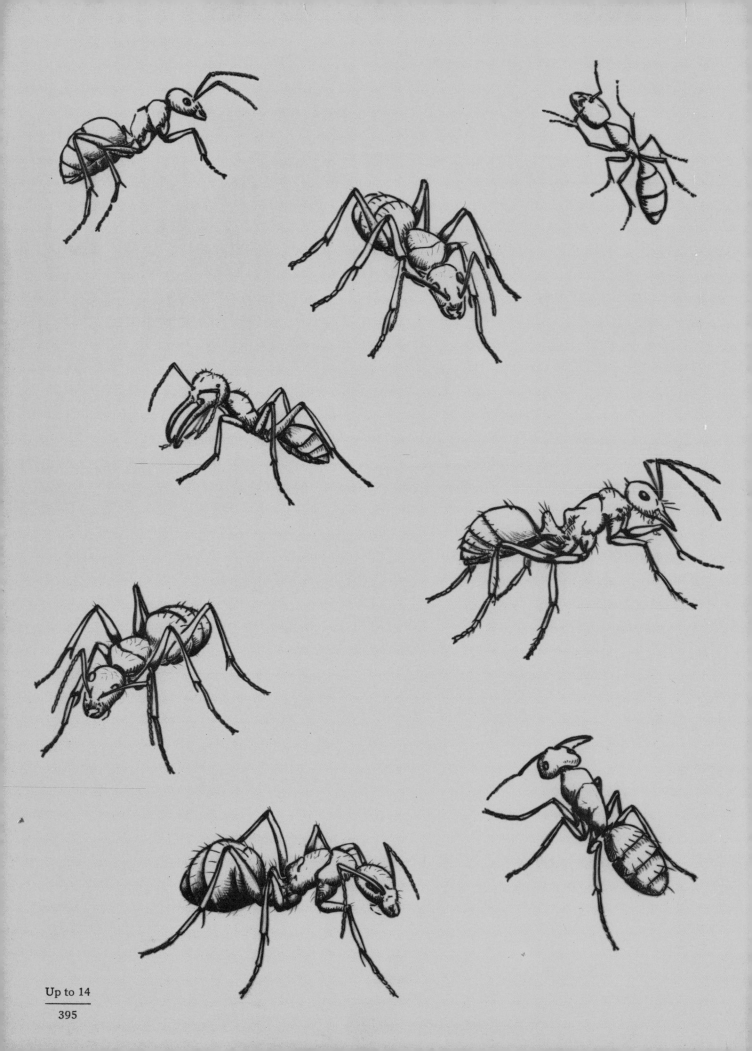

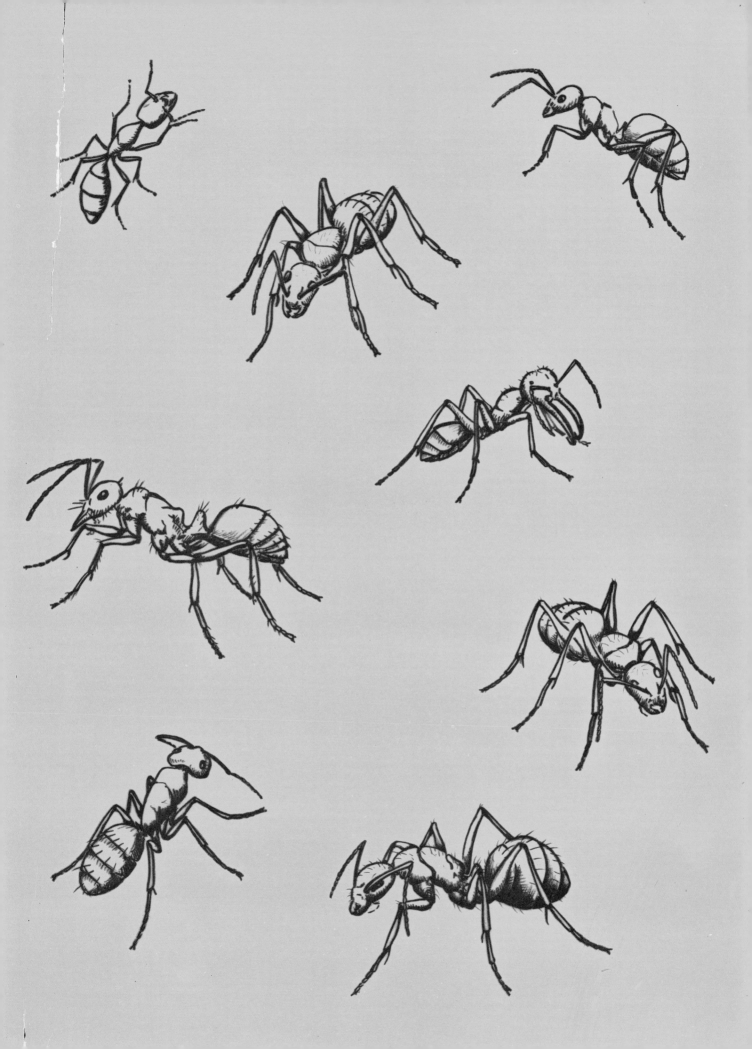

THE STORY OF ANTS

By Dorothy E. Shuttlesworth

Illustrated by Su Zan N. Swain

Parade of leafcutter ants
(*Atta texana*)

THE STORY
OF ANTS

DOUBLEDAY & COMPANY, INC.
GARDEN CITY, NEW YORK

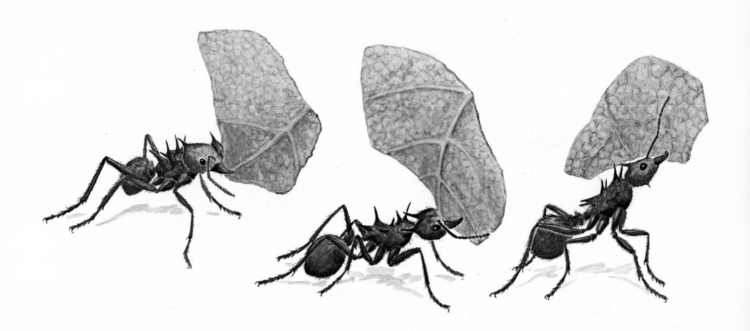

For William N. Hall,
who long has been an inspiration
to artist and author
and who first suggested this book.

Sincere appreciation is extended to F. J. Bartlett for
fire ant material; to the Department of Entomology of
The American Museum of Natural History for making
available the ant specimens used for the illustrations;
to Sugi Noguchi for the decoration on pages 8 and 9
and the diagrams on page 12; and to Minosuke
Noguchi for the calligraphy on page 18.

CONTENTS

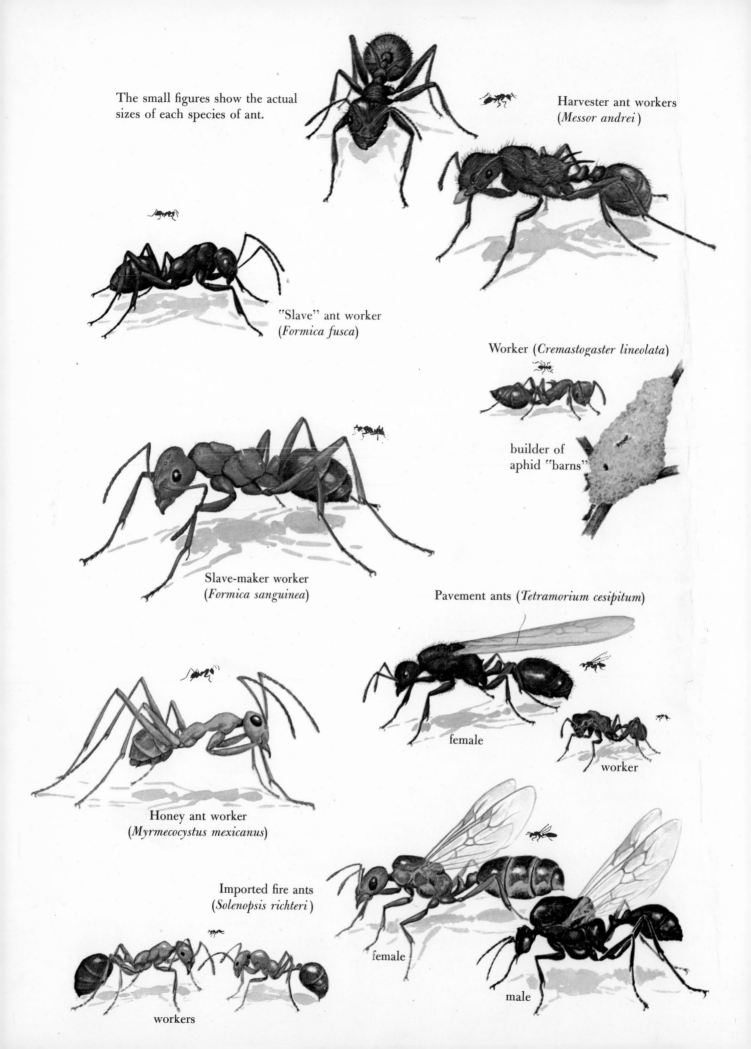

The small figures show the actual
sizes of each species of ant.

Harvester ant workers
(*Messor andrei*)

"Slave" ant worker
(*Formica fusca*)

Worker (*Cremastogaster lineolata*)

builder of
aphid "barns"

Slave-maker worker
(*Formica sanguinea*)

Pavement ants (*Tetramorium cesipitum*)

female

worker

Honey ant worker
(*Myrmecocystus mexicanus*)

Imported fire ants
(*Solenopsis richteri*)

female

male

workers

Pharaoh's ants (*Monomorium pharaonis*)

workers

queen

INTRODUCTION

More than a hundred million years ago there were some kinds of ants scurrying about on the earth much as they do today. A hundred million years! In this great length of time many other kinds of animals came into being, flourished for a while, then died away leaving only fossil remains as evidence that they ever existed. It is not surprising, therefore, that we sometimes wonder about the success of these little insects.

In general, people are apt to think that ants thrive because they are constantly busy. Certainly their reputation for industry is widespread, being noted even in Biblical times when King Solomon gave the advice, "Go to the ant, O sluggard, consider her ways and be wise." Because the quotation often is ended here, it may be thought that the mere hustle and bustle of ants were the only "ways" Solomon had in mind. But the words that follow concern a harvest, and indicate that the King was thinking of an ability to provide for the future during fair-weather months. However, it is not likely that he really had an understanding of all the remarkable ways of ants. Did he know that some kinds do not harvest but eat only meat, while others keep plant lice as "cows," obtaining nourishment through them? Did he realize that certain ants enslaved others? Did he know of the fine cooperation between the members of an ant colony and of their talents in constructing homes and caring for them?

Probably not a great deal was known of the life history of ants in the long-ago days of Solomon, but through the years many scientists have watched and studied them. Even people who were not scientists found the little ant fascinating, and endless facts have now been recorded by people who have "considered her ways." In fact, ant-watching today has become a popular hobby. Not only are ants observed in their natural settings, but a variety of homes have been invented so that colonies can be brought indoors and watched under comfortable conditions. Ready-made nests may be bought at hobby or pet shops, and there are several "do-it-yourself" types which can be made at small expense.

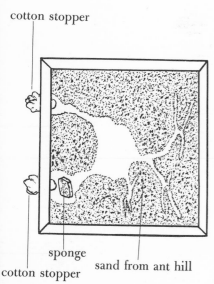

cotton stopper

sponge

cotton stopper   sand from ant hill

Two views of ant house
with hinged cover

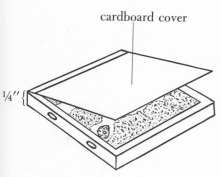

cardboard cover

¼″

One excellent homemade ant house can be made of two square pieces of glass held apart by four strips of wood set around the edges. The height or thickness of the strips should be chosen according to the size of the expected ant tenants. A quarter of an inch is the most likely to be needed; an eighth-inch strip is often enough. The first step in its construction is to get the two pieces of glass, each about ten inches square. Then cut the strips of wood to the appropriate length. One piece of glass is placed flat on a table and strips of wood are cemented around three sides of it. Before the fourth strip of wood is glued into place, drill two small holes in it several inches apart as shown in the diagram. These openings will serve to supply the ants with food and water. Cotton plugs will keep the ants from escaping. After the cement has dried, the glass area should be well filled with fine, sifted earth, except in the center and near the two openings.

Now for the ants! If you wish to watch the entire cycle of ant life, it is necessary to secure a queen as well as workers. A queen may be recognized by her size—in many species very large in comparison with her workers. Colonies may be found beneath logs, stones, and debris, and they should be hunted with a shovel and plastic bag. Queen and a few workers should be scooped up gently but quickly, placed in the bag, then taken to their new quarters. After they are transferred this time, the second square of glass must be quickly placed on top of the wood strips and fastened with tape.

Into the "water hole" is inserted a moistened bit of sponge. Into the "food hole" go small bits of food such as bread, cookies, honey, and cake icing. The holes are kept plugged except to renew the moisture on the sponge and to remove unused food before it becomes moldy, replacing it with fresh.

The ant home should be completed by binding all edges with adhesive tape, then covering the top with a piece of cardboard slightly larger than the glass, and binding it along one edge with a piece of tape for a hinge. This provides the ants with the darkness necessary for them to live normally. It may be lifted when you want to watch the ant community in action.

If your ant group includes a queen, you may see the entire cycle of life—from egg to adult. But even without a queen, the workers are both interesting and amusing to watch as they make tunnels, lick themselves clean, sleep, stretch, and partake of the food and water you have provided. They are perhaps the smallest yet most active "pets" you could hope to find.

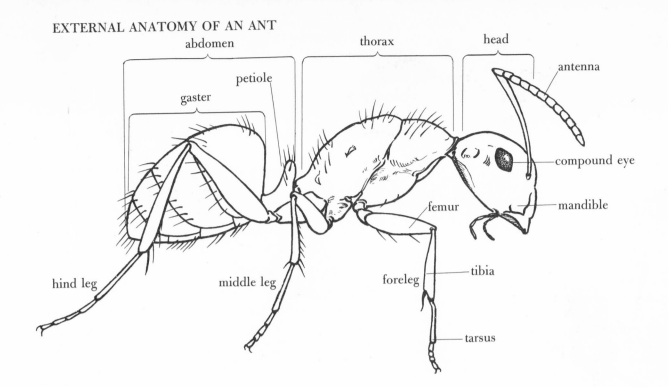

EXTERNAL ANATOMY OF AN ANT

abdomen · thorax · head

gaster · petiole · antenna

compound eye

mandible

femur

hind leg · middle leg · foreleg · tibia

tarsus

HOW TO RECOGNIZE AN ANT

Almost everyone thinks he knows an ant when he sees one. But does he? Of course the general form of this little insect is widely recognized: its narrowed "waist" and prominent feelers give it a definite and distinctive form. However, the question often is raised, "How can you tell the difference between an ant and a termite?" It then becomes apparent that people do not always know the difference between ants and certain other creatures.

Because of the many interesting similarities and differences between ants and termites, the termite story will be discussed later in this book. But besides the termites, there are reasons for confusion between ants and a number of other insects. For example, ants with wings are produced only at certain seasons of the year and, as a result, people are inclined to forget that ants ever take this form and mistake flying ants for wasps.

Then, as a turn-about tale, we have a wasp that is often mistaken for an ant. In fact, its popular name is the "velvet ant," because the wingless females of these wasps look so much like ants covered with yellow, red, or black velvet. However, the "velvet" is actually a mass of hair and the "ant" is really a wasp. Their sizes vary from a tiny eighth of an inch in length to a full inch or more.

Confusion as to identity is often created by the fact that a variety of insects move into ant nests to live. Some of them cause no trouble to their hosts; others do. But friend or foe, they often look so much

13

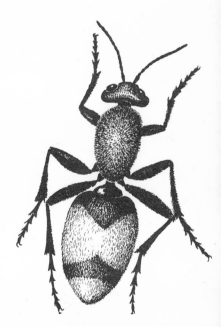

Although popularly called "velvet ant," this insect is really a female wasp.

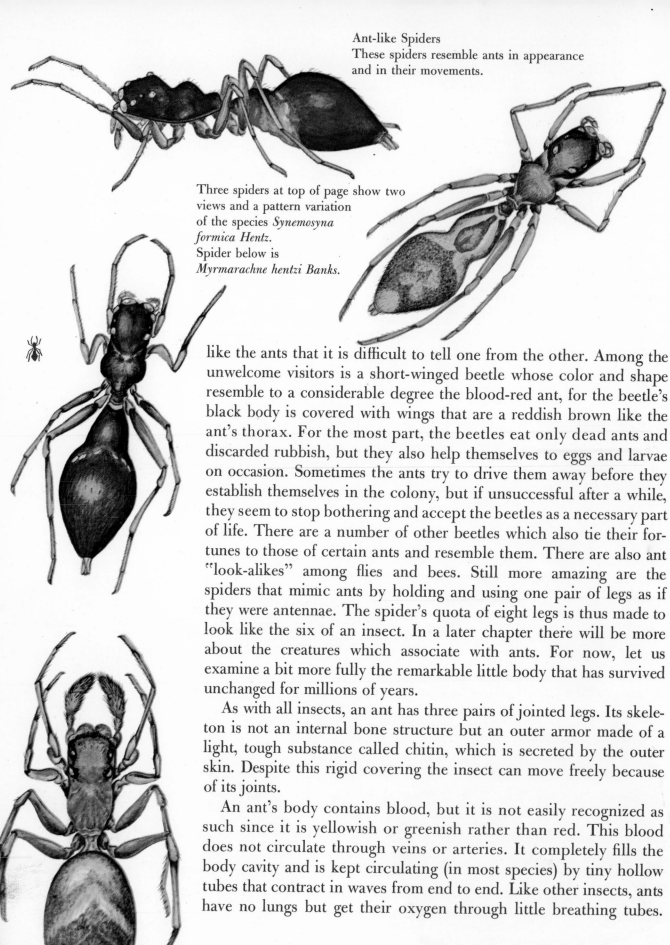

Ant-like Spiders
These spiders resemble ants in appearance
and in their movements.

Three spiders at top of page show two
views and a pattern variation
of the species *Synemosyna
formica Hentz*.
Spider below is
Myrmarachne hentzi Banks.

like the ants that it is difficult to tell one from the other. Among the
unwelcome visitors is a short-winged beetle whose color and shape
resemble to a considerable degree the blood-red ant, for the beetle's
black body is covered with wings that are a reddish brown like the
ant's thorax. For the most part, the beetles eat only dead ants and
discarded rubbish, but they also help themselves to eggs and larvae
on occasion. Sometimes the ants try to drive them away before they
establish themselves in the colony, but if unsuccessful after a while,
they seem to stop bothering and accept the beetles as a necessary part
of life. There are a number of other beetles which also tie their for-
tunes to those of certain ants and resemble them. There are also ant
"look-alikes" among flies and bees. Still more amazing are the
spiders that mimic ants by holding and using one pair of legs as if
they were antennae. The spider's quota of eight legs is thus made to
look like the six of an insect. In a later chapter there will be more
about the creatures which associate with ants. For now, let us
examine a bit more fully the remarkable little body that has survived
unchanged for millions of years.

As with all insects, an ant has three pairs of jointed legs. Its skele-
ton is not an internal bone structure but an outer armor made of a
light, tough substance called chitin, which is secreted by the outer
skin. Despite this rigid covering the insect can move freely because
of its joints.

An ant's body contains blood, but it is not easily recognized as
such since it is yellowish or greenish rather than red. This blood
does not circulate through veins or arteries. It completely fills the
body cavity and is kept circulating (in most species) by tiny hollow
tubes that contract in waves from end to end. Like other insects, ants
have no lungs but get their oxygen through little breathing tubes.

The body is made up of three distinct parts—head, thorax, and abdomen. Inside the little head is the insect's tiny brain, sometimes no more than a fraction of a millimeter in size.

On winged types of ants, such as males and queens in proper season, there are two pairs of wings (one pair longer than the other) attached at the top of the thorax. In the abdomen of workers in most species, there are two stomachs, one of which is called the crop or "social stomach." Here the ant stores food as she finds it. Later she may pump it out again to feed her companions. To be digested the food must be pumped into the true stomach. Also in the abdomen are the poison glands from which a pain-giving fluid can be released. In certain species of ants there is a true stinger like that of a bee.

As you look closely at an ant's body, it may seem there is an "extra" part between body and abdomen. However, this is only a connecting segment that actually belongs to the abdomen. Certain species have two such segments. These extra segments or segment, called the petiole, form the distinctive waist.

A knowledge that ants have survived on earth in the same form for millions of years has been given us through a study of fossils. In the era that followed the Age of Dinosaurs, a great variety of insects developed. There were also pine trees from which oozed sticky sap, and often this hardened into a stone that is called "Baltic amber." Many times insects were trapped in the gummy substance, and were fossilized as it hardened. Tiny flies and beetles are well represented among them, but they are surpassed by the ants. It seems that ants were actually the most abundant of all insects in that long-ago time and they have kept this "upper hand" in the animal kingdom to the present day. Here is one kind of animal that has not been displaced or vanquished by people. Ants thrive under our very feet as well as in jungles, deserts, woodlands, and meadows.

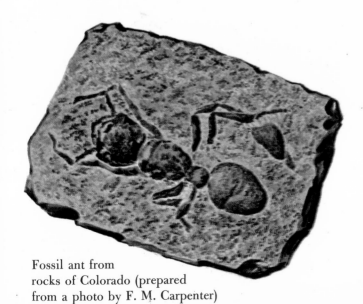

Fossil ant from
rocks of Colorado (prepared
from a photo by F. M. Carpenter)

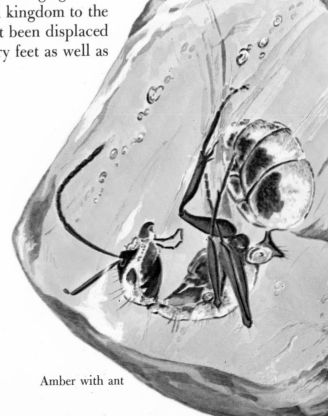

Amber with ant

THE TRUE "STINGERS"

As with all kinds of animals, ants have a variety of relatives. There are the very closely related—the sisters, brothers, and parents—and there are the members of the same species which may live far apart from each other but are alike in all important respects. Others, with certain variations, do not belong to the same species but are closely enough related to be classed in the same genus; and within the same genus may be a large number of different species. Beyond the genus is the family—perhaps divided into subfamilies—and beyond the family group is the order. Taking this broad view, it seems that every creature in the animal kingdom is bountifully supplied with relatives. Yet, even considering all the links that relate one animal to another, it is still astonishing to realize the numbers of close relatives an ant may claim.

First of all, ants are related to all insects that belong to the order Hymenoptera, and in the Hymenoptera we find more than a hundred thousand different species. To it belong not only ants, but bees and wasps and certain other social insects. In fact all of the truly social insects (those that live and work in groups), except for the termites, are included.

What are the features that make an insect a member of Hymenoptera? We find that all members have two pairs of wings—wings that are transparent and are crossed by a few simple veins. The hind pair are somewhat smaller than the front, and are held to the front wings by tiny hooks. Even though the wings are small in proportion

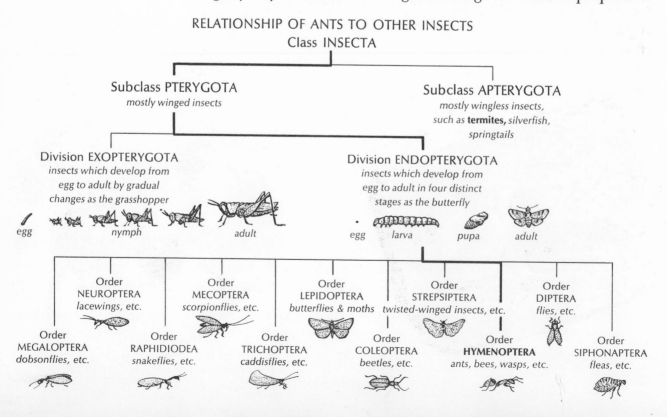

RELATIONSHIP OF ANTS TO OTHER INSECTS
Class INSECTA

Subclass PTERYGOTA
mostly winged insects

Subclass APTERYGOTA
*mostly wingless insects,
such as* **termites,** *silverfish,
springtails*

Division EXOPTERYGOTA
*insects which develop from
egg to adult by gradual
changes as the grasshopper*

egg   *nymph*   *adult*

Division ENDOPTERYGOTA
*insects which develop from
egg to adult in four distinct
stages as the butterfly*

egg   *larva*   *pupa*   *adult*

Order
NEUROPTERA
lacewings, etc.

Order
MECOPTERA
scorpionflies, etc.

Order
LEPIDOPTERA
butterflies & moths

Order
STREPSIPTERA
twisted-winged insects, etc.

Order
DIPTERA
flies, etc.

Order
MEGALOPTERA
dobsonflies, etc.

Order
RAPHIDIODEA
snakeflies, etc.

Order
TRICHOPTERA
caddisflies, etc.

Order
COLEOPTERA
beetles, etc.

Order
HYMENOPTERA
ants, bees, wasps, etc.

Order
SIPHONAPTERA
fleas, etc.

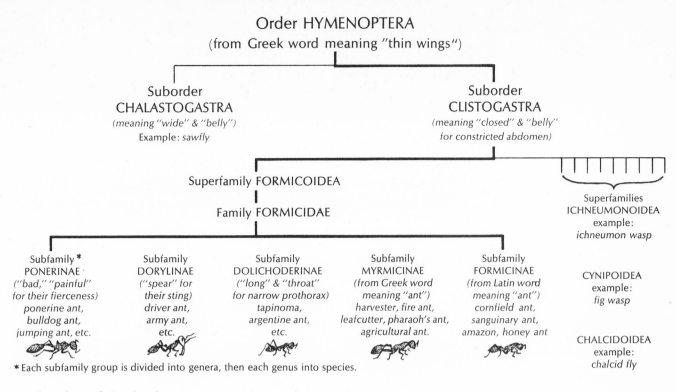

Order HYMENOPTERA
(from Greek word meaning "thin wings")

Suborder CHALASTOGASTRA
(meaning "wide" & "belly")
Example: *sawfly*

Suborder CLISTOGASTRA
(meaning "closed" & "belly"
for constricted abdomen)

Superfamily FORMICOIDEA

Family FORMICIDAE

Subfamily * PONERINAE
("bad," "painful"
for their fierceness)
*ponerine ant,
bulldog ant,
jumping ant, etc.*

Subfamily DORYLINAE
("spear" for
their sting)
*driver ant,
army ant,
etc.*

Subfamily DOLICHODERINAE
("long" & "throat"
for narrow prothorax)
*tapinoma,
argentine ant,
etc.*

Subfamily MYRMICINAE
(from Greek word
meaning "ant")
*harvester, fire ant,
leafcutter, pharaoh's ant,
agricultural ant.*

Subfamily FORMICINAE
(from Latin word
meaning "ant")
*cornfield ant,
sanguinary ant,
amazon, honey ant*

Superfamilies ICHNEUMONOIDEA
example:
ichneumon wasp

CYNIPOIDEA
example:
fig wasp

CHALCIDOIDEA
example:
chalcid fly

SERPHOIDEA
example:
plalygasterid parasite

BETHYLOIDEA
example:
bethylid wasp

CHRYSIDOIDEA
example:
cuckoo wasp

SPHECOIDEA
example:
solitary wasp

VESPOIDEA
example:
hornet

APOIDEA
example:
bee

*Each subfamily group is divided into genera, then each genus into species.

to the size of the body, many members of the order are strong flyers. (The females of some species are exceptions in having no wings at all.) With many members of the order the body is divided into three distinct regions—head, thorax, and abdomen. The mouth parts are of the biting type. And this order is the only one in which the insect may have a genuine stinger.

There is always a great deal of interest in "stingers" since they cause so much misery to the human race, and people wonder at the difference between an insect sting and a bite. A mosquito really does bite, and it sucks blood—the females of most species having piercing, sucking mouth parts. It does not sting. The ants, wasps, and bees which do, use an organ concerned with egg-laying, called the "ovipositor." A great many ants sting, and most of them bite as well, with their very efficient jaws. Some not only bite but squirt an acid into the wound they have made. The jet may be sent out with a force that carries it as much as two feet. The sting of certain ants is very painful indeed, even more so than that inflicted by a honey bee.

In the great order Hymenoptera we find insects with two different types of body. On one there is a broad base to the abdomen where it is joined to the thorax. On the other, the abdomen is constricted at one point so that the insect has a "pinched waist" look. Ants belong to the second group, and the slender waist is one of their most easily noticed features. The slender-waisted group of Hymenoptera bears the name Clistogastra from the Latin *clistos* (closed) and *gastros* (belly). The ants themselves have the family name Formicidae.

When we separate the ants from all other Hymenoptera, we still find fantastic numbers and varieties. To date more than eight thousand different species, subspecies, and varieties have been seen and described, and these live in colonies which may be composed of a few dozen or hundreds, or thousands, or hundreds of thousands of individuals. Ants outnumber every other land-living creature (those large enough to be seen easily) in the world. They flourish practically everywhere—from arctic regions through the tropics, and on down close to the antarctic, from timber line to high mountains, and from desert sands and seashore to damp forests.

Because of their vast numbers and the wide variety of climates in which they live, it is not surprising to learn that ants have many different modes of life. However, it would still take a lively imagination to guess at the many different ways in which ants make a living. Some are gardeners, actually growing their own food. Some are "dairy farmers," keeping plant lice known as aphids from which they obtain a sweet fluid by "milking" them. Some are hunters and spend their lives foraging in restless armies. Some are savage fighters and some are expert at carrying out slave raids. Among their amazing abilities we find they can construct nests with a complicated maze of chambers and corridors in earth or wood; they can build bridges with their own bodies; and some of them can actually sew.

In the Japanese language the word ant is made by combining the character for "insect" and the character for "unselfishness, justice, and courtesy." Here is evidence that ants are regarded with real admiration by some peoples. Nevertheless there are doubtless many in Japan as well as in other areas who view these insects with dismay because of the destruction they cause. But whatever feelings they call forth, ants are worthy of study. They cannot fail to inspire wonder at nature's marvels, and to invite a comparison of their community form of life with the social behavior of man.

 Insect

 Ant

 just
unselfish
courteous

The two Japanese characters at the left, one meaning insect and the other standing for a number of virtues, combine and form the word "ant."

This ant (*Colobopsis impressa*) lives in plant stems and closes the entrance to its nest with its face, which is especially adapted to act as a "stopper." At the right is a twig with the front of the ant's face blocking the entrance.

BACKYARD EXPLORING

The term "ant hill" is known so generally it is easy for someone to have an idea that all ant homes are concerned with mounds of earth. However, this is far from true, as you will realize when you notice crowds of these insects emerging from cracks in a cement sidewalk or on lawns where no "hills" exist. No, in spite of ant mounds—both the small and those of spectacular size—some ants nest under a flat surface, possibly with a stone for their "roof." They may also be found nesting in hollow stems of plants, in tree stumps and pine cones, under the bark of tree trunks, in crevices of walls, and in all sorts of unlikely places. Once I was startled to find that a large colony had taken over the interior of a sleeping bag while it was stored for the summer. Ants do have need of a certain amount of warmth and humidity, and those that live in cool, wet areas find ways to combat too much dampness. In hot, dry regions they ventilate their nests so efficiently they may be said to enjoy "air-conditioned" homes. One thing is quite certain: no matter where you live, ants are not far away. In cities they may be found in parks, and in suburbs and country your hunting grounds are unlimited. Indeed there is always the unhappy chance that they will come exploring in your home before you get outside to look for theirs.

On the trail of ants you may look for a flat stone of fair size in a sunny area of any typical backyard. If you turn over such a stone, the chances are good that an ant nest will be revealed, and quite possibly the occupants will be the kind named *Lasius niger*. This species

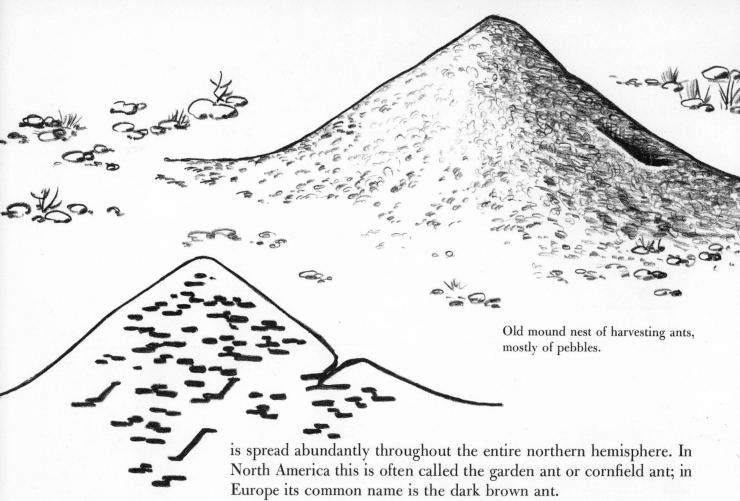

Old mound nest of harvesting ants,
mostly of pebbles.

Cross-section of the
nest showing chambers
and connecting galleries.

is spread abundantly throughout the entire northern hemisphere. In
North America this is often called the garden ant or cornfield ant; in
Europe its common name is the dark brown ant.

As the stone is turned back, exposing a colony to sudden bright
light, you will see the worker ants in swift motion. Their immediate
concern is for the larvae and pupae—the coming generation. Seizing
the tiny wormlike "babies" in their jaws, they rush deeper into the
ground, using the tunnels they have constructed with great care. If
the observer has a magnifying glass to use, or is especially keen of
eye, he may note that the pupae (rather than the larvae) are often
rescued first. Adults will soon develop from them.

Somewhere in the nest will be one ant very much larger than the
rest (if the nest is of unusual size, there may be several rather than
one) and this is the queen. When a queen is starting a new colony,
she entrenches herself in the ground and soon produces a new generation. The ant workers that appear begin excavations at once, making
tunnels and larger, cleared areas that are called galleries. At first this
may not seem so remarkable, but as time goes by and work continues,
the nest grows into a really complicated structure. Into some galleries
go eggs (these are so small that a magnifying glass is usually needed to
see them); in others larvae and pupae are stored. Still other galleries
are provided for storing food.

Most of an ant's building activities are accomplished with claws
and the outer jaws known as "mandibles." These powerful though

small jaws, placed at either side of the head, in most ants have rough, toothed edges—almost like tiny, pointed teeth. It seems that the best time for the insect workers to dig and carry earth is after a shower when the soil is well dampened, with just enough moisture to make it easy to handle. Pellets of the soil are scooped up in the mandibles and some of them are carried out of the nest where they are left in cone-shaped piles. Other soil pellets are molded into brick-like form by the ant's forelegs, and the "bricks" are patted into a spot that helps to form the wall of a tunnel or gallery. After a wall has been built, the insects then must turn to the more complicated task of securing ceilings. Just how they do this is something of a puzzle to architects and scientists alike!

Ledges are the next project. The little builders start these on opposite walls and extend them until they meet. In some ant nests the rooms thus formed may be two or more inches in width. Such construction is a large order for the little workers. Sometimes, too, the galleries have vaulted ceilings, which often have the support of pillars.

Once a nest has been established it might seem that construction work would end, but such is not the case. Small improvements are made constantly. Besides the building that goes on, the walls are kept "scrubbed," the galleries neat and clean. And the tunnels are often alive with workers carrying larvae and pupae from one gallery

Workers attending young.

to another as they seek the best possible temperature for their charges. Thus community life goes on busily and productively. The nest is carefully guarded, with entrance or entrances closed with soil during the night or watched by vigilant worker-soldiers. It would appear such a colony was "set" for all time.

Very often, however, ants seem to show a liking for change—some species being more inclined to this than others. A colony may be functioning smoothly in a good location when, for reasons not always known, a group of its members move to a spot a little distance away that seems to be better for a home. Thereupon they start a second nest, then return to their first established home and, seizing the queen and young, carry them triumphantly to the new quarters. Interestingly enough, all the ants of a colony may not take part in the move. Some resist the change. Such stubborn-acting characters are usually picked up and carried off by their more restless fellow-workers.

But the contest of wills does not necessarily end even then, for members of the resistance movement are likely to get busy and carry pupae and larvae back to the first home. This is the signal for the pioneer type to begin again; for the second time they remove all to the new headquarters. Now there may be a back and forth shuttle between the two nests—a double procession of ants on the march in opposite directions, bearing the upcoming generation in their jaws! The dispute, though it does not involve any fighting, may continue

Ant workers attending aphid "cows."

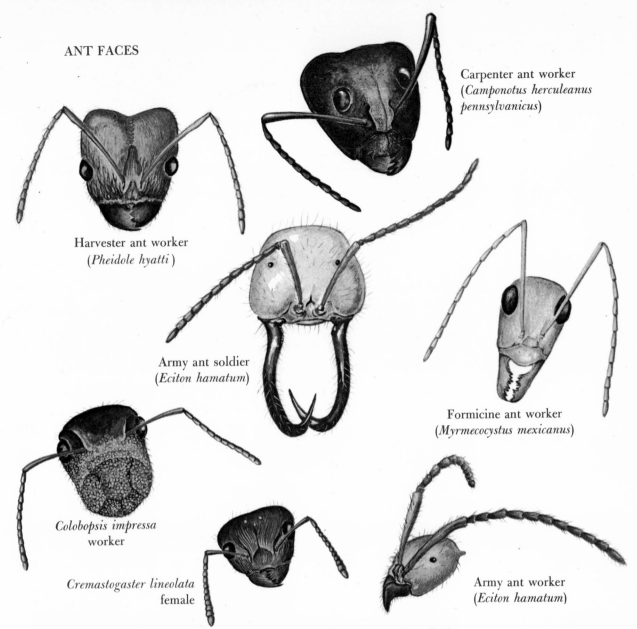

Carpenter ant worker
(*Camponotus herculeanus
pennsylvanicus*)

Harvester ant worker
(*Pheidole hyatti*)

Army ant soldier
(*Eciton hamatum*)

Formicine ant worker
(*Myrmecocystus mexicanus*)

Colobopsis impressa
worker

Cremastogaster lineolata
female

Army ant worker
(*Eciton hamatum*)

for days or even weeks. At last one side grows discouraged and gives up its opposition. The colony then becomes united, usually in the new home, for the ants that moved first nearly always win.

When you are "backyard exploring" in search of ant life, it could be that you are close to a nest without knowing it, for often the entrances are hidden by leaves or twigs. But watch the little creatures hurrying about on their endless quests to discover where they disappear regularly, and you doubtless will locate a colony. If it were possible to look inside the nest without disturbing it, just what activities would be revealed? Of course this would depend somewhat upon the kind of ant and the stage of development of the colony. But in our next chapter let us consider a usual type of colony from its beginnings to know what there is to be discovered at one time or another.

A QUEEN AND HER SUBJECTS

In colonies of nearly every species of ant there comes a time when a new group of queens and males are produced, along with new workers. When they mature, both the queens and males have wings. Fully developed, they remain in the nest until one warm day (often when there is rain in the air, and generally toward evening) when, as if at a given signal, they move out for the marriage flight. All the colonies of a certain species for miles around usually "get the message" at about the same time, and the winged leaders set forth, accompanied by excited workers to their take-off positions on stones and plants. Soon the air is filled with flying ants.

In some areas the number of individuals involved in marriage swarms is almost not to be believed. South American observers have reported several thousand males and many thousands of queens of leaf-cutter ants coming from a single nest. Europe, too, is the scene of tremendous swarms. In Germany the hordes that rise over trees and hilltops have been dense enough to resemble smoke, causing people to call warnings to nearby fire departments!

The marriage flight lasts but a short time. After fertilization has taken place, males and females are soon back on the ground, and at this time many fall prey to birds and other kinds of insect-eating creatures. It matters little if the males do lose their lives in this fashion for they are doomed anyway. Those that escape enemies die very quickly as their strength is gone and they do not have the ability to hunt for food.

How different is the fate of females! A queen-in-the-making may take a short rest after floating back to earth, but soon she is ready to start her career. Her first task is the removal of her wings. She may

winged female

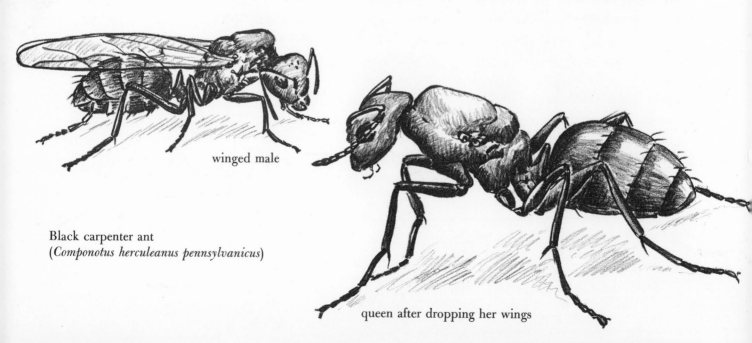

Black carpenter ant
(*Componotus herculeanus pennsylvanicus*)

winged male

queen after dropping her wings

accomplish this by bending sideways and pressing the wings against stones or grass blades and stretching them in a way that causes them to break off. Sometimes she pulls at them with her legs. Even if the wings stubbornly refuse to come loose with this rough treatment, they soon begin to shrink and before long are shed as a natural process.

Wingless, the queen is ready to start her colony. Whether she is the kind that lives in wood or in the earth, her actions in general are the same. She finds a site to her liking and excavates a burrow—a little closed chamber into which she shuts herself and begins a truly lonely existence. For many weeks or perhaps months she remains there waiting for the eggs inside her to mature. From time to time she may make slight improvements in her burrow, but otherwise is inactive. She has nourishment chiefly from the fat wing muscles that are no longer needed for their original purpose. Little by little their fibers shrink and the substance is released into her body. Finally she begins to lay eggs, and, completing a fascinating circle in the food-supply story, she eats a number of them and so builds her strength further.

Soon the eggs that have escaped the hungry queen develop into wormlike larvae, and now the founder of the colony has new duties. She must feed the growing youngsters. This she does with her saliva, laden with nutriment. Very efficiently she concentrates on the largest of the larvae, giving it the major share of food. The second largest receives second best treatment and so on down the scale. As a result a few of the brood grow very quickly.

As the larvae grow, they burst through their skins and shed them. This happens three or four times, at which point they have almost reached their full growth. Still they are not adult. Each must now spin a cocoon about itself, and in this pupal stage it rests as it changes into a grown-up ant. After a few weeks the adults are ready to emerge, and again the queen mother is on the job. She helps them

eggs

larvae

cocoon

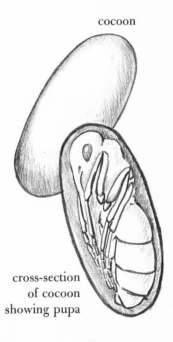

cross-section
of cocoon
showing pupa

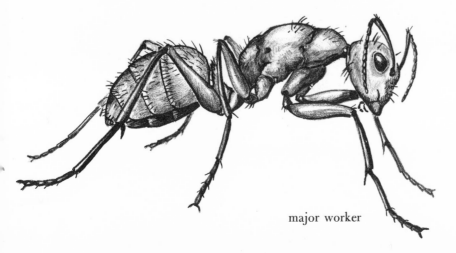

major worker

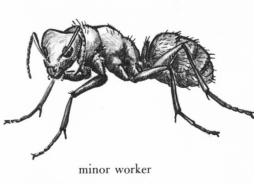

minor worker

Carpenter ant queen attending to her first brood.

shed their wrappings, cleans, and feeds them. Then at last her energy and patience are rewarded; she has workers to help in what has been a very lonely task.

The first workers of a colony are usually smaller than those that will be born later, but their size is not an indication of their ability. They are ready for action almost at once and very soon are able to dig themselves out of the burrow. Probably startled by the bright light on the surface, they scurry about until they encounter a small insect that can be overpowered and dragged into the nest. The arrival of "real" food signals a new phase in the life of the colony as it causes the babies still in the larval stage to develop rapidly. And now the queen's long fast comes to an end; she is fed and tended by her willing subjects. No longer will she play the role of a brave pioneer. The only duty left to her is egg laying, and this she may do for a number of years. Another mating-flight is never necessary because she has become fertile for life.

The first group of workers to be produced with many kinds of ants have very brief lives, but while they are doing their bit for the colony's future, larger and better-nourished members are developing. The workers are considered to be female; however they are females that are imperfectly developed.

With its working group established, an ant colony becomes thoroughly organized. As eggs are laid the workers take immediate charge of them, massing numbers of the pin-point small objects together so that they form a compact bundle. Even after they develop into larvae—curious little white creatures, legless and with curved bodies —they continue to hang together. For a while the workers feed them,

26

giving them food which is already partly digested. Then as they develop they can take, without help, bits of food that are brought to them. When almost as large as they will be in adult form, they are ready to pupate.

In many species, the larvae prepare for the pupal stage by spinning themselves into cocoons much as butterfly and moth caterpillars do. The pupae, each about the size of a small wheat grain and looking like a tiny sack tied at one end with a black string, are often mistakenly called ant "eggs." They are sold in many pet shops under this name, being used as fish and bird food.

After the young have reached the pupal stage, the "nurse" workers still continue to be responsible for them. A proper temperature is important to their welfare, and during the heat of the day the workers move their charges to galleries deeper in the ground. With the coolness of evening they carry them up again, nearer the warmth of a pavement or the earth's surface. Another chore is keeping them clean; the nurses lick both pupae and larvae with careful attention. When a nest is attacked, these workers form a rescue team to rush the young to a safe hiding place.

After the pupal stage has been completed (the length of time required varies with different species, but is usually around three weeks) the worker ants have new duties. In many cases they help remove the cocoon and pupal skin and often they help the newborn to straighten out their cramped legs and antennae. Then they may move them into the most desirable positions in the nest by locking jaws and dragging them, or by pulling them by leg or neck. Newly hatched adults are known as "callows." Their color is pale, with eyes very dark in contrast to their body.

With some kinds of ants (those that are not as specialized in their

Newly emerged worker called "callow" (light in color) with other older workers.

ways) the workers show no real interest in helping pupae on to their adult stage, but they do give some aid nevertheless. When pupal skin is being shed, it forms one more source of food for the busy workers. The adults, therefore, nibble at the skin as it comes loose and when (as often happens) it sticks to the pupae in some spots, they are a real benefit to the struggling youngsters.

In general there are said to be three kinds of individuals in the population of every colony: queen, workers, and males. However, there are actually more than three types because there are sometimes several kinds, or castes, of workers. Some are giants or supersoldiers; some are pygmy soldiers, and some undersized workers.

Though the name "soldier" suggests an especially warlike or vicious ant, this is not necessarily the case under all conditions. The soldier acts or serves as a defender of the home. It has an unusually large head and thick head armor protected by a hard skin. Its jaws, too, are larger and stronger than those of the ordinary worker. Despite all these features to its advantage, the soldier usually is not very aggressive except when there is some great disturbance. It thrusts its head against the entrance to its nest to keep out would-be intruders, and it can give a good account of itself fighting enemies or capturing prey. However, among meat-eating ants it usually is the other workers which make the first attack; the soldiers engage in the battle only after it has been started. Then their powerful jaws are put to use, and a victim may be torn to bits in short order. Soldiers usually do not concern themselves with carrying food back to the nest, but sometimes they are involved with domestic chores. Among certain species the soldiers take part in licking the larvae clean and in carrying them from one part of the nest to another when it seems best to do so.

Carpenter ant workers helping
a young ant shed its cocoon.

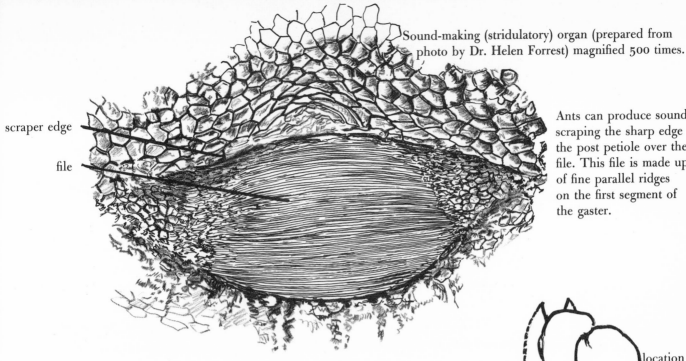

Sound-making (stridulatory) organ (prepared from photo by Dr. Helen Forrest) magnified 500 times.

scraper edge

file

Ants can produce sounds by scraping the sharp edge of the post petiole over the file. This file is made up of fine parallel ridges on the first segment of the gaster.

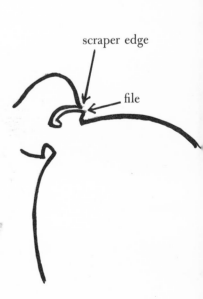

location of sound-producing organs.

scraper edge

file

With one type of carpenter ant, which lives in trees, the head of the soldier actually is shaped like a stopper. These colonies live in tree branches and a head "stopper" is thrust into any hole through which enemies might enter.

Considering the variety of castes that make up a colony and the various colonies that are situated close by each other, we must marvel at the way all the individuals know without mistake "who is who." In other words, there is a sureness in each ant as to where it belongs and which other ants form its immediate family. The secret of this knowledge is in smell or scent, for each species has its own particular "brand" and each nest (even nests of the same species) has its own special odor.

The equipment which enables an ant to recognize odors is the antennae or feelers. There are two of them projecting from the head, and each consists of a long single joint (the shaft) and a section (the lash) made up of a number of small joints—anywhere from nine to thirteen. Organs of smell and touch are located in these segments. With them, because of the extreme sensitivity to odors which they provide, an ant can orient herself in many ways: she recognizes her own nest and nest-mates, her queen, and the members of the brood in their various stages of development. Antennae are of critical importance. If an ant loses the terminal segments, her ability to participate as a member of the colony is greatly reduced.

You may often notice ants, either in a man-made observation nest or out of doors, using their antennae to feel their way—investigating any obstacles that lie in their paths. They also appear to "talk" with this marvelous equipment as two individuals meet and stand together with antennae fluttering, and even cross their feelers and pat each other with them. It is amusing to speculate that some neighborly gossip is taking place! Between one thing and other, the antennae are constantly in motion. They are by far the most important sensory organs that ants possess. Nerve fibers connected with them carry information to the brain and thus an ant is made aware of what needs to be done in carrying out its various chores.

Grooming is another activity connected with the antennae that provides a good show for any interested observer. An ant cleans this very sensitive equipment thoroughly and regularly. On its front legs are hairs, which form a neat brush, and the little insect usually begins grooming by lifting a leg over one antenna, and pulling the antenna through the brush. It then cleans the brush by pulling it through the mouth. The second antenna is treated in the same manner, and there might be several more swipes on each side.

During the winter in northern regions, ants have a well-earned rest. As the ground begins to grow cold and hard, the many individuals of a colony huddle together in their underground retreat and sleep away the months until spring warmth stirs them to action again. But even during hibernation their instinct for self-preservation may be revealed as the tight ball formed by their bodies churns endlessly. The churning is caused by the individuals actually walking in their sleep as those on the outer rim move toward the center for greater warmth. In the center of the mass—and never displaced—is the queen.

Members of the ant-worker caste may live for several years. The queens have an even longer life span; records show that they often achieve an age of twelve years or more.

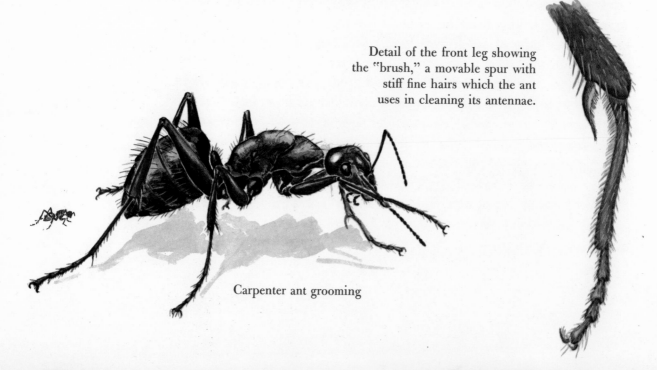

Detail of the front leg showing the "brush," a movable spur with stiff fine hairs which the ant uses in cleaning its antennae.

Carpenter ant grooming

Workers of American Amazon ants

THE SLAVE MAKERS

Ants are industrious and often peaceful; many go about their work in complete independence, never intruding on others. But some ants are much more aggressive. They are bold raiders that invade the nests of other species, fight the adults, and carry off the young to their own nest where the captives are made into slaves.

"Slave raids" are every bit as dramatic as they sound. Let us see how one is carried out by large, handsome, brownish red ants called Amazon (*Polyergus rufescens*). When the time is ripe for a raid, a number of the Amazon warriors group outside their own nest, then rapidly and without hesitation march toward the colony marked for attack. Usually this will be a nest of black-colored ants (*Formica fusca*). Here they may become engaged in fierce combat—if the black ants are inclined to do battle. As the Amazons pierce the heads and bodies of their victims with sharp, sickle-shaped jaws, the black ants, with their duller jaws, gnaw desperately at the legs of their enemies. But no matter how fierce the combat, the Amazons are not turned back from their goal, which is the pupae of the black ants. Soon a number of these are captured and carried to the victors' home, where they are carefully stowed away until they develop into adults. From then on they are fated to spend their lives working for the Amazons, finding them food, feeding them, and sometimes even helping raid a nearby nest that was their original home!

31

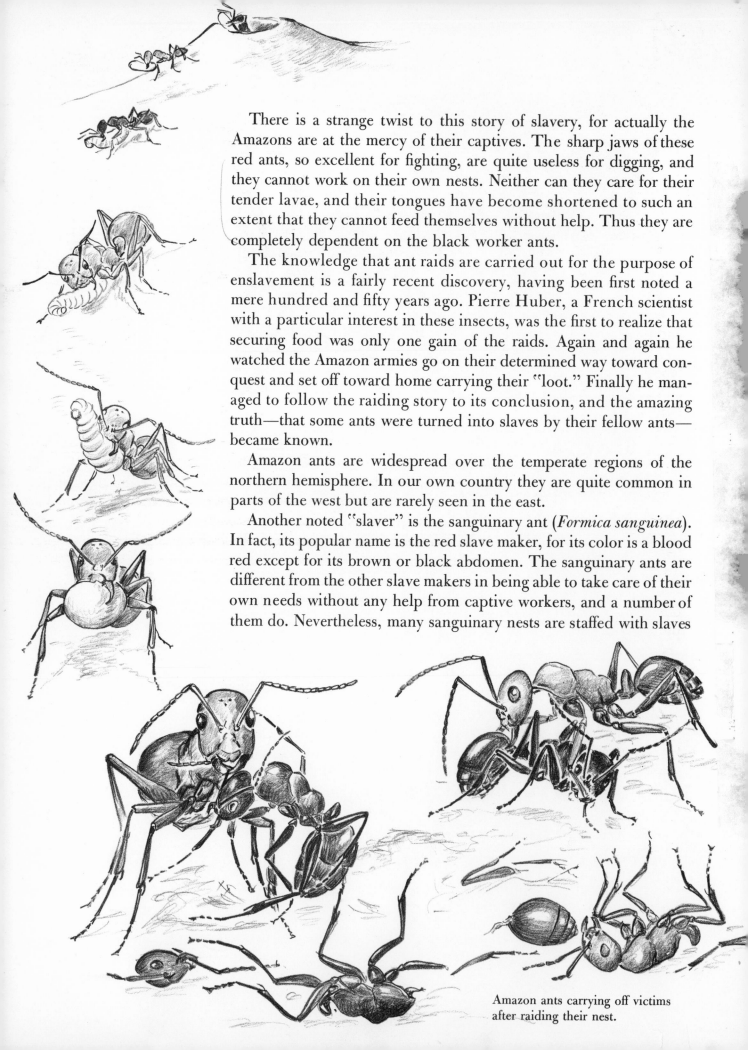

There is a strange twist to this story of slavery, for actually the Amazons are at the mercy of their captives. The sharp jaws of these red ants, so excellent for fighting, are quite useless for digging, and they cannot work on their own nests. Neither can they care for their tender lavae, and their tongues have become shortened to such an extent that they cannot feed themselves without help. Thus they are completely dependent on the black worker ants.

The knowledge that ant raids are carried out for the purpose of enslavement is a fairly recent discovery, having been first noted a mere hundred and fifty years ago. Pierre Huber, a French scientist with a particular interest in these insects, was the first to realize that securing food was only one gain of the raids. Again and again he watched the Amazon armies go on their determined way toward conquest and set off toward home carrying their "loot." Finally he managed to follow the raiding story to its conclusion, and the amazing truth—that some ants were turned into slaves by their fellow ants— became known.

Amazon ants are widespread over the temperate regions of the northern hemisphere. In our own country they are quite common in parts of the west but are rarely seen in the east.

Another noted "slaver" is the sanguinary ant (*Formica sanguinea*). In fact, its popular name is the red slave maker, for its color is a blood red except for its brown or black abdomen. The sanguinary ants are different from the other slave makers in being able to take care of their own needs without any help from captive workers, and a number of them do. Nevertheless, many sanguinary nests are staffed with slaves

Amazon ants carrying off victims after raiding their nest.

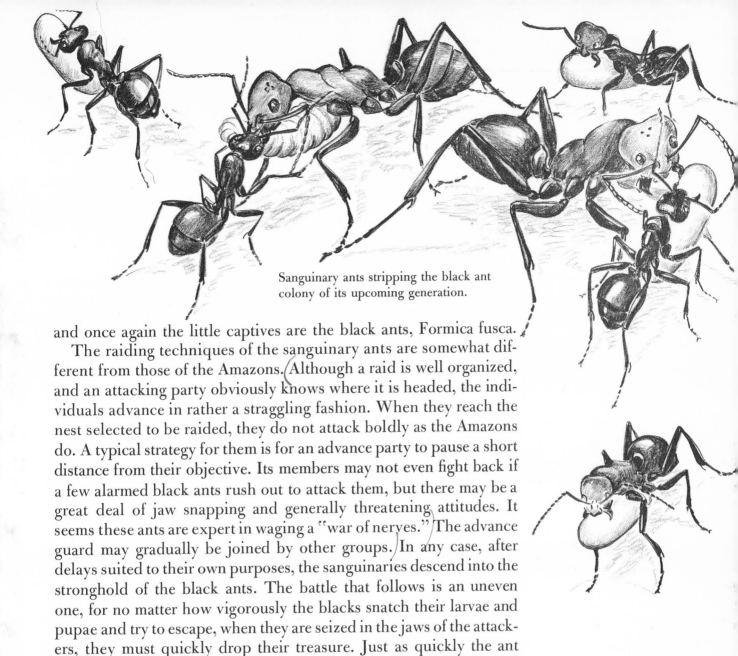

Sanguinary ants stripping the black ant colony of its upcoming generation.

and once again the little captives are the black ants, Formica fusca.

The raiding techniques of the sanguinary ants are somewhat different from those of the Amazons. Although a raid is well organized, and an attacking party obviously knows where it is headed, the individuals advance in rather a straggling fashion. When they reach the nest selected to be raided, they do not attack boldly as the Amazons do. A typical strategy for them is for an advance party to pause a short distance from their objective. Its members may not even fight back if a few alarmed black ants rush out to attack them, but there may be a great deal of jaw snapping and generally threatening attitudes. It seems these ants are expert in waging a "war of nerves." The advance guard may gradually be joined by other groups. In any case, after delays suited to their own purposes, the sanguinaries descend into the stronghold of the black ants. The battle that follows is an uneven one, for no matter how vigorously the blacks snatch their larvae and pupae and try to escape, when they are seized in the jaws of the attackers, they must quickly drop their treasure. Just as quickly the ant infants are seized by the raiders, which usually do not bother to kill their opponents so long as they get what they went after. Soon the sanguinaries have stripped the colony of all its upcoming generation and their homeward trip, carrying this prize, is made in an apparently joyful spirit. They move with what has been described as a "peculiar cantering motion."

Back at their own nest, the victors are welcomed excitedly by their stay-at-home sisters. The captured larvae and pupae are taken inside, and, while some may be eaten at once, most of them are carefully stowed away where they can grow into useful slaves.

And what of the ransacked black ant colony? All of the workers that have not been disabled lose no time in starting to rebuild their little world. So long as they have a queen and possibly a few rescued

33

larvae and pupae, their plight is not hopeless. Before long they achieve a new or rebuilt home. Some unlucky colonies, however, are raided season after season. And sometimes the greedy sanguinaries not only rob a colony of its coming generation, but they seem to decide the nest is better than their own. After a raid has been accomplished, they move "bag and baggage" (actually queen, eggs, larvae, pupae, and food) into the plundered nest.

Besides the slave raids, ants have some other extraordinary ways of staffing a colony. One of these concerns the kidnaper-type ant which steals into a nest of some closely related species, piles up all the pupae and stays with them, keeping the rightful family at a distance. When ants emerge as adults, they are loyal to the kidnapers! However, the two species may continue to live in one colony.

Another sneak-attack (which is really not an attack at all) is carried out by a few species of small yellow ants which simply move into the home of a closely related species and make friends with the workers. Before long these workers murder their own queen and serve the needs of the "friendly" invaders. In time they die off—and the newcomers are in full possession.

In Africa lives a sinister character known as the "decapitating ant." A fertile queen of this species flies to the nest of a much larger ant—*Tapinoma* by name. Landing near the entrance, she waits patiently until worker *Tapinomas* come out to investigate. As a rule they seize the loitering stranger and drag her into their home, but oddly enough they do not eat her. She then climbs on the back of the queen of the colony and saws at her neck until the head falls off. The *Tapinoma* workers serve the "decapitator" as if she were their own queen and care for the eggs she soon produces. In time her offspring are able to carry on the work of the nest, which after a while is populated by decapitating ants only. Similar events take place among certain ants in other parts of the world, as well as in Africa.

Decapitating ant of Europe (*Teleutomyrmex schneideri*) starting her deadly work on a pavement ant queen (*Tetramorium cespitum*).

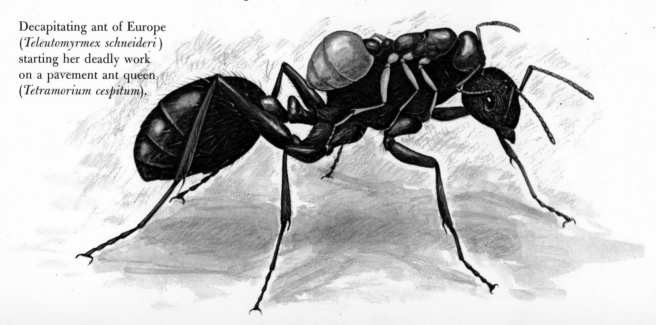

CARPENTERS AND HONEY ANTS

Carpenter ants, interesting as they are, will never be popular. And with good reason! Their special talent of boring into wood often destroys not only good trees but buildings, and causes damage such as that done by termites. Though they do not eat wood, as termites do, they chew out the fiber to make chambers in which to live. Many times they take over a location where termites have lived but died away, and carry on their activities in the same area.

The black carpenter (*Camponotus pennsylvanicus*) is one of our largest native ants. The size of the workers varies, but they may be a full half inch in length. The queen measures nearly an inch.

Living in a natural setting, carpenter ants would not be particularly destructive since, for the most part, they would seek out old logs and stumps in which to tunnel. However, as forests have been disappearing they have been adapting themselves to life with people.

Honey ants of North America (*Myrmecocystus horti-deorum*) clinging to the root of the gallery of the nest. They act as living storage pots for other members of the colony.

Below these are shown two workers, one with distended gaster bearing nectar.

35

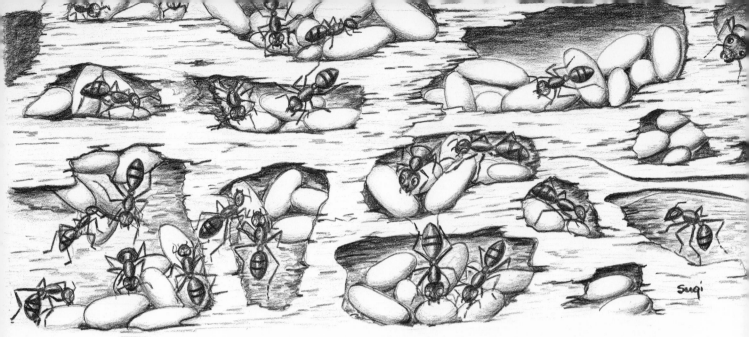

Nest of carpenter ants, made in wood.

And not only may a large colony weaken the structure of a house, but there is the ever-present prospect of finding them invading bread boxes, cookie jars, and other food supplies. An added cause for their unpopularity is the carpenter's inclination to give a nasty bite with its sharp and powerful jaws.

Our native carpenter ants often travel to Europe, their passage being achieved in timber shipped from America. For some reason, however, they do not settle in homes there as they do on our own continent. The "herculean" ant is the largest species of this type found in Europe.

A species closely related to the carpenter ant is the *Colobopsis*. This kind establishes its colonies in trees. Often the white ash is chosen, with the queen gnawing her way into the soft pith of some convenient shoot. In Central Europe, however, the upper branches of various nut trees seem to be preferred for nesting.

Colobopsis is distinguished for the truly remarkable way its nest is guarded. Certain of the workers, larger in size than the rest, have a head that is especially thick and flattened. This makes a perfect plug, and nearly always there is a plug headed guard stopping up the entrance to the nest. When another worker wants to leave, the guard backs away so this may be accomplished. And when a member of the colony wishes to return home, at a tap on the head of the guard with its antennae, the "doorway" opens. The guard undoubtedly recognizes the familiar colony odor on the outside before uncorking the entrance.

A really notable relative of the carpenter ant is the black honey ant, *Camponotus inflatus.* While its popular name may suggest that this insect seeks out the kind of honey we store on pantry shelves, such is not the case. It does live on "honey," but it is a particular kind—an

36

ant "honeydew," thin, almost colorless, and lacking the rich flavor of bee honey. This valued food substance has two origins. One is the sweet sap of plants that has been sucked out of them and passed through the ant's body. The other is created by tiny plant lice known as aphids. The aphids suck juice from roots, stems, and leaves. Then as they partially digest this sap it becomes sweeter in taste than it was originally, and the ants lick it from their bodies.

Many ants eat honeydew, and some kinds make it their complete diet. Such ants have a problem, for in dry climates fresh supplies are not always available. The solution is to store honey, and certain desert-living species have developed such a successful storage system they have earned the name of "honeypots" (*Myrmecocystus*).

If we look into the home of a colony of honeypot ants, we would at first see a normal enough situation, with queen, workers, and undeveloped grubs. However, if we look beyond and below the regular living chambers, we will discover other, larger rooms several feet beneath the surface of the ground. Hanging from their ceilings are strange, potbellied creatures. In general appearance there is a resemblance to the other worker ants, but the hind part of the body is huge —out of all proportion to the rest of their form. And these swollen abdomens are filled with ant honey! It has been put there by the normal workers which collect the plant juices, then pump honey into their living storage tanks. This type of feeding begins when the honeypots are young enough for their skin to stretch; those that are fated for storage are set apart for life to serve this one purpose. They cannot walk, in fact can scarcely move, but hang from the ceilings of the especially constructed chambers, receiving honey and giving it out again when the need arises.

Not always, however, do the ants reap the benefit of their careful work. In Mexico the honeypots are sometimes hunted by people, dug out of the ground, and served at feasts as a special delicacy.

Honey ants gathering nectar which exudes from a gall formed as a result of a wasp laying its egg. This wasp is very tiny, its gall is about the size of a pea.

Carpenter ant worker on the underside of a sunflower leaf. It is gathering "honeydew," which the tree hopper larva exudes. At the right is an adult tree hopper.

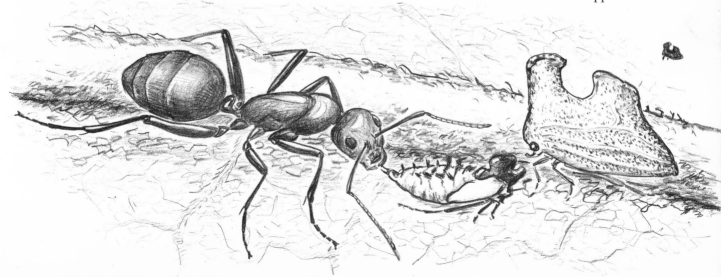

winged male

winged female

worker

A VARIETY OF TALENTS

On the whole ants may be said to need a "well-balanced diet," for as people do, they require carbohydrates, proteins, and fats. Thus it may seem strange that certain kinds have food "specialties." Some, such as the harvesters, eat mostly starch, some subsist chiefly on the sugar that they take from plant saps; some are meat eaters. However, no matter which type of diet is followed, there is a degree of conversion of the food within the body of the ant so that it has all the elements needed for a good "balance."

Some ants, as we have seen in the preceding chapter, store honey in the bodies of certain members of their colony so that their sugar supply never becomes exhausted. Amazing this may be, but still more complicated is the system worked out by certain species to secure honey from plant lice known as aphids.

Because of the way ants use them, such aphids are known as ant "cows," and their honey is sometimes called "milk." They possess long sucking tubes with which they drill into plants and draw out juices—more than their bodies can use. The clear, sweet surplus is dropped out from the tip of the abdomen, and may simply flow over a nearby leaf. Or an ant meeting an aphid will lick the honey directly from its body. Often, however, meetings with aphids are not left to chance; the ants capture a number of them, care for them, and, in proper season, "put them out to pasture." Thus their supply of honey is assured.

On our own continent one of the most widespread of the "cattle-tending" species is the cornfield ant, *Lasius niger americanus*. Its efficient method of operating makes it a serious pest to farmers. When a colony has been established, it loses no time in making an alliance with a certain kind of aphid that specializes in attacking corn plants. Throughout the winter the cornfield ants store the eggs of this aphid in their nest, meanwhile keeping a number of adults close-by, on the roots of grasses which they can reach by means of tunnels. In the spring when corn plants have made a good start, the ants transfer the aphids to their roots. Since the aphids breed with startling rapidity (sixteen generations may be produced between mid-spring and late fall) a cornfield may be quickly doomed by their presence. To make matters still more serious (from the farmer's point of view) as a plant dies, the ever-watchful ants remove all the aphid pests from it and transfer them to a healthy plant!

Besides keeping and tending "cows," the ants actually "milk" them, doing so by stroking and tapping the belly of the aphid with their antennae in a certain special way. All in all, such ants may be considered very expert "dairy farmers." Little do they realize that in their success they have become enemies of human farmers who are striving to raise corn crops.

Not all the aphids used by ants are kept in this dairy-farm manner. Some species keep their "cows" close at hand simply by carrying captive aphids from one leaf to another as they travel about; often they cut the wings off winged aphids to prevent their flying away. Another system is to make underground galleries around roots and stock them with "herds" of aphids. Or an outdoor "barn" to shelter aphids may be made by ants, using materials such as wood, bark, or mud. It is built on trees or bushes, often a considerable distance from the ant nest. When this is the case, the little insect builders may connect nest and barn with a covered corridor.

The ever-surprising ant has more talent for farming than merely dairy management. There are species—the harvester ants—that store seeds underground, and other species—the fungus-growing ants—that plant their own small gardens underground.

The harvester ants, numerous in many parts of our own country, in the Far East, and in Africa, manage stored crops with great efficiency. And very likely it was to this kind that King Solomon

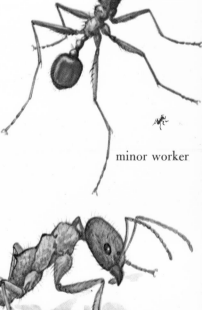

Harvester ants
(*Pheidole hyatti*)

minor worker

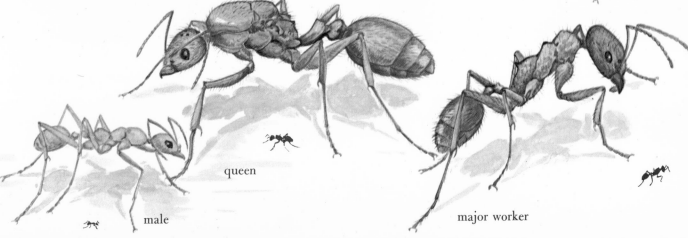

male

queen

major worker

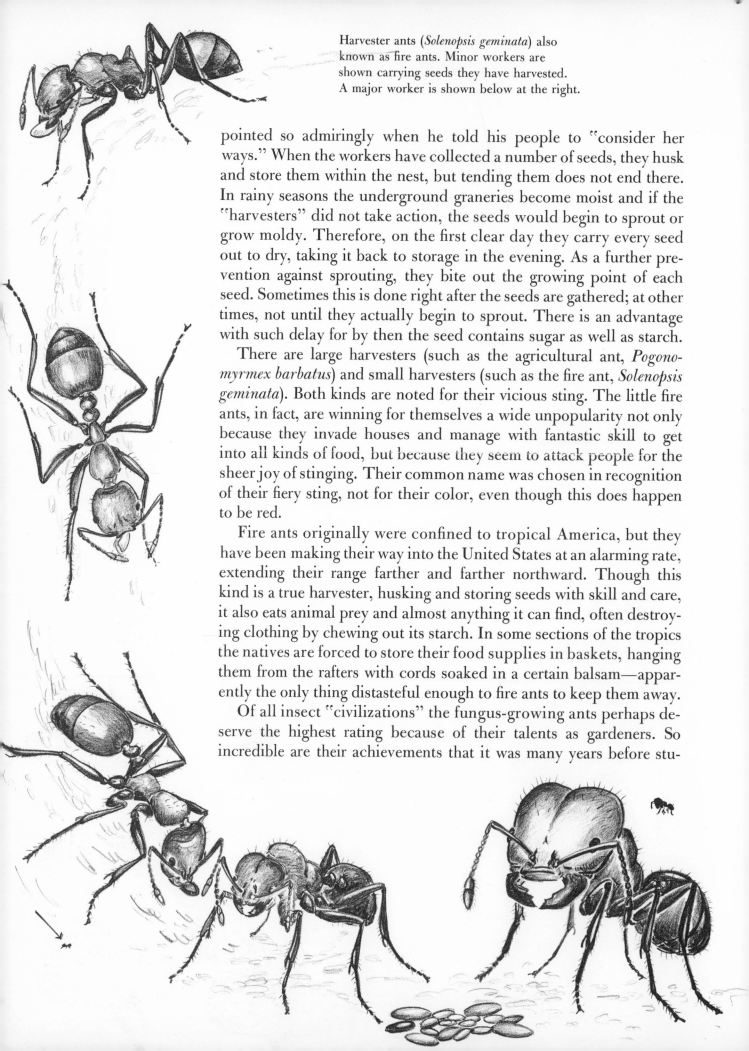

Harvester ants (*Solenopsis geminata*) also known as fire ants. Minor workers are shown carrying seeds they have harvested. A major worker is shown below at the right.

pointed so admiringly when he told his people to "consider her ways." When the workers have collected a number of seeds, they husk and store them within the nest, but tending them does not end there. In rainy seasons the underground graneries become moist and if the "harvesters" did not take action, the seeds would begin to sprout or grow moldy. Therefore, on the first clear day they carry every seed out to dry, taking it back to storage in the evening. As a further prevention against sprouting, they bite out the growing point of each seed. Sometimes this is done right after the seeds are gathered; at other times, not until they actually begin to sprout. There is an advantage with such delay for by then the seed contains sugar as well as starch.

There are large harvesters (such as the agricultural ant, *Pogonomyrmex barbatus*) and small harvesters (such as the fire ant, *Solenopsis geminata*). Both kinds are noted for their vicious sting. The little fire ants, in fact, are winning for themselves a wide unpopularity not only because they invade houses and manage with fantastic skill to get into all kinds of food, but because they seem to attack people for the sheer joy of stinging. Their common name was chosen in recognition of their fiery sting, not for their color, even though this does happen to be red.

Fire ants originally were confined to tropical America, but they have been making their way into the United States at an alarming rate, extending their range farther and farther northward. Though this kind is a true harvester, husking and storing seeds with skill and care, it also eats animal prey and almost anything it can find, often destroying clothing by chewing out its starch. In some sections of the tropics the natives are forced to store their food supplies in baskets, hanging them from the rafters with cords soaked in a certain balsam—apparently the only thing distasteful enough to fire ants to keep them away.

Of all insect "civilizations" the fungus-growing ants perhaps deserve the highest rating because of their talents as gardeners. So incredible are their achievements that it was many years before students of ant behavior could accept for a fact that these insects actually did plan and produce fungus gardens to grow the food they desired. The true fungus growers (species of *Atta* and *Acromyrmex*) found in Central and South America, first attracted attention because of their leaf-cutting activities. These ants can be literally devastating. They march in apparently endless hordes to a tree, and each one cuts a good-sized circular piece from a leaf. The ants are often so numerous that not only may a single tree be quickly stripped of its foliage, but whole plantations may be ruined by them in a short time.

For a long time observers wondered what ants could possibly do with such quantities of leaves, which obviously were not meant to be eaten by them. At last close observation and unexpected discoveries revealed the secret: once inside the nest the ants chew the leaf sections into a spongelike mass which they store in a special chamber far under the earth's surface. This is the so-called fungus or "mushroom" garden from which their crops will spring.

Crops are not a matter of luck; the ants give their gardens remarkable care. If leaves brought to the nest are too dry, they are left outside overnight to absorb moisture. If they are too damp from rain, they are left above ground until somewhat drier. If a hard rain soaks them too thoroughly, they are abandoned and a new supply is collected. As the little farmers stow the chewed leaves underground, they make passages and hollow areas in the large masses which they can open and close as desired to regulate ventilation and temperature.

The leafcutters are widely known by the name "parasol ants," because when returning home with a round piece of leaf held overhead, each one appears to be carrying a little sunshade. But *Atta* ants are far from being delicate, as the need for a parasol might suggest. Every member of a colony is well armored with prickles. The soldiers have extremely powerful jaws which can give a nasty bite even into human flesh. However, Indians in Central America often put these trouble-makers to an interesting use. If one of them has a bad cut, he finds some soldier parasol ants, then draws the flesh along his wound close

41

Cross-section of nest showing galleries with fungus gardens.

together and places the ants, one by one, along the severed flesh. The ants bite, and, in so doing, draw together the edges of the flesh. When enough ants have been used to mend the cut, their bodies are twisted until they break off from the heads. Even this treatment does not cause the jaws to relax, so the flesh is held firmly until it has a chance to grow together again.

Another kind of ant that "sews" things together is found in southern Asia and on some of the Pacific Islands. But this type, the *Oecophylla,* is not forced into the activity; by "sewing" these ants build nests of leaves. To start their project a group of workers station themselves along the border of one leaf and, with their jaws imbedded in the edge of the leaf next to it, pull the two close together. While the leaves are held close, other workers carry to the scene of action a number of larvae which are able to produce silk by means of tiny glands in their heads. Each adult ant gently squeezes the larva it is carrying (with the result that activity is stimulated in the silkmaking glands) and then firmly presses the larva against the foliage to be "sewn."

As soon as a strand of silk has been glued to the edge of one leaf, the worker moves the larva over to the next leaf, and the thread is anchored there. Back goes the worker to the first leaf with its larva, and the same process goes on over and over until the two leaves are quite firmly joined. A single worker may manage the leaf-sewing with only one assistant or, when leaves are far apart, a large number of ants may combine forces to accomplish the task.

Unusual in looks as well as in actions, the *Oecophylla* has many green members. These include the queens and some workers, while other workers are reddish and the males black. They are fairly large, measuring from a quarter to nearly a half inch in length, and they are extremely warlike. Other insects cannot survive in a tree which they have taken for their own, and anyone investigating their remarkable nests must be on guard against a furious stinging and biting onslaught from the "sewing" ants.

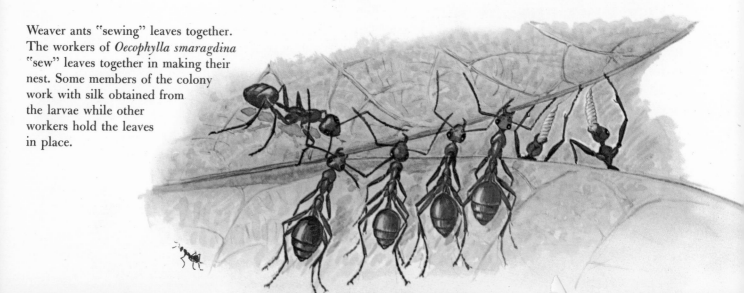

Weaver ants "sewing" leaves together. The workers of *Oecophylla smaragdina* "sew" leaves together in making their nest. Some members of the colony work with silk obtained from the larvae while other workers hold the leaves in place.

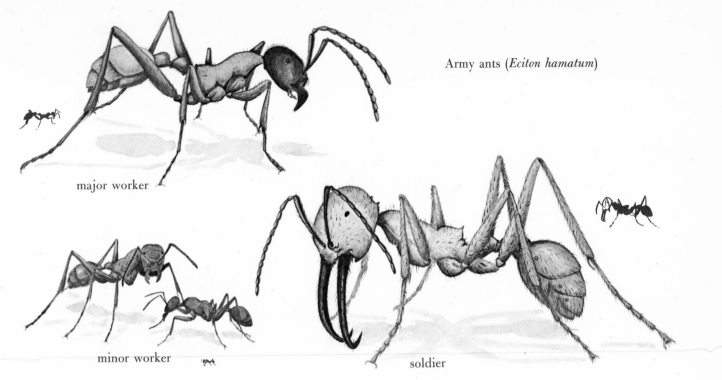

Army ants (*Eciton hamatum*)

major worker

minor worker

soldier

THE NOMADS

Ants that construct elaborate homes and tend gardens and store harvests in bins of their own making may arouse our keen interest, but other ants that do none of these things are even more startling. These are the meat eaters and hunters, which track down prey and often destroy animals many times larger than themselves. Their accomplishments often seem frightening and frightful; they make perfect material for writers of horror stories. As a result, much has been written about them, and often by people who are not interested in being accurate but only in telling a "good story." So let us look at some of the known facts about the ants that hunt for a living, many of which have no permanent home but are almost constantly on the move.

One nomad is the "bulldog" ant (of the genus *Myrmecia,* with many different species) of Australia. The popular name of this insect is based on its powerful jaws. Besides the painful bite it can inflict, it has a vicious stinger, perhaps a quarter of an inch long. The bulldog is among the largest of ants. An additional hazard so far as its victims go is that it can make a ground-clearing jump, sometimes leaping as much as a foot. Some species of bulldog ants do make simple mound nests, others live beneath stones, but all kinds hunt tirelessly, roaming far and wide. Although many of the nomads work in great swarms, the bulldog ants usually work alone, and even a single individual may subdue other insects much larger than itself. In some

43

cases they hunt in groups and carry out devastating raids against other ants and termites.

Bulldogs and other species that hunt and live in small colonies are in a subfamily with the name Ponerines. In another group, called the Dorylines, are the spectacular army ants and the driver ants. The dorylines live mostly in tropical regions but they are found to some extent in other areas as well. In North America the species are small and belong chiefly to southern states. It is tropical America and Africa which have the mighty legions.

True army ants make no nests and have no regular home. When on the march, the workers carry the larvae in their jaws. The queens, instead of laying their eggs continuously as happens with other types, produce them in great batches at regular intervals. When the larvae are mature and spin cocoons, the colony pauses in its travels for some time—usually about three weeks. About midway during the long stop, a new batch of eggs is laid; within a week the queen will produce tens of thousands. After about ten days the pupae have matured, and their emergence from the cocoons excites the colony once more to a nomadic activity. With many big "pushes" this nomadic phase continues, and each day the colony carries on a large, vigorous raid, and each night it migrates to a new location. Meanwhile the new brood has developed into tiny larvae that excite the colony still further.

The doryline ants of Africa (known as driver ants) have remarkably large colonies, and they often cause great destruction. The swarm at the head of a raid is often several yards wide. It is made up of count-

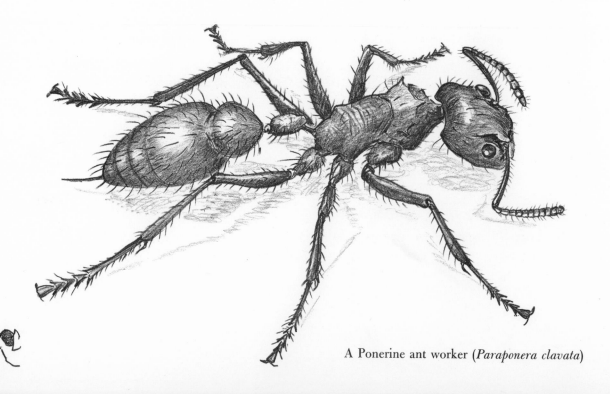

A Ponerine ant worker (*Paraponera clavata*)

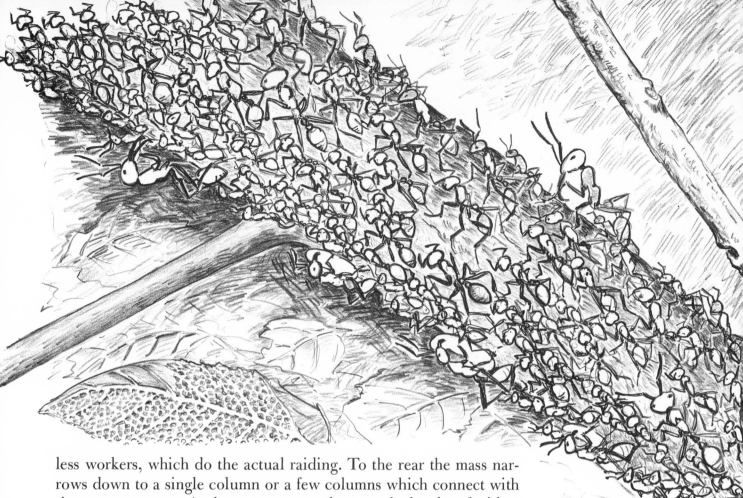

Army ants on the march.

less workers, which do the actual raiding. To the rear the mass narrows down to a single column or a few columns which connect with the temporary nest. As the great swarm advances, the hordes of raiders cover the trunks of tall trees, invade all kinds of holes in the ground, and even take over human dwellings for a time. So great are their numbers it is almost impossible to find any means of stopping their onslaught.

The organization of an ant army is the height of efficiency. Workers in the forefront are constantly making short advances, then turning back, to be followed immediately by the individuals that had been behind them, and each successive group progresses a little farther forward. The forward sweep of the mass is literally a huge relay process.

A swarm of driver ants is made up of individuals of many types, from minute workers to the large workers or soldiers, although more of the raiding is done by workers of intermediate size. These ants are most efficient in bringing great numbers to bear on a new victim; they are excited by its movements and odor. Their accomplishments seem all the more remarkable when we realize that driver ant workers are completely without eyes. The males do have large eyes, but the queens have neither eyes nor wings.

Nothing but meat is of interest to driver ants. As they swarm over the countryside, small "game," such as other insects and often snakes,

45

mice, and rats, is devoured to the vanishing point. Larger victims may even be crocodiles, deer—almost any creature unlucky enough to be trapped so that it cannot make a quick getaway. When they ransack a farm, every bit of meat (except bacon, for they do not like salt) and the flesh of live animals is seized, while other foods such as butter, sugar, cheese, and cake, which would delight many ants, remain untouched.

Another fact, besides their lack of eyes, that would seem to be an almost fatal handicap to these armies of driver ants, bothers them not at all: direct sunlight will kill them in a very short time. Mostly they manage this problem by traveling and working at night and during dull, rainy days. When circumstances seem to require action on a sunny day, they move through thick grass or heavy tree foliage. Sometimes, when caught suddenly by the sun, they hurriedly construct a covered archway of earth, thrown up from both sides of their moving column.

In Africa in the type of moist, low-lying areas where driver ants thrive, there are many streams to be crossed. Ants are not swimmers, but usually they are able to make their way from one side to the other on some natural bridge. Once in a very long time something remarkable happens in that they form a bridge with their own bodies. Such an operation begins with a great mass of them clustering at a spot on one bank, perhaps where a root or shrub juts out. Quickly a number of individuals link their bodies together while some of the large soldiers with the most powerful jaws hold fast to an object on the

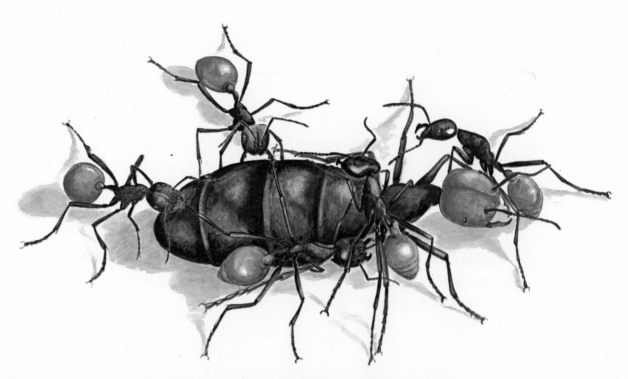

Army ant workers (*Eciton burchelli*) attending the queen (prepared from kodachrome by T. C. Schneirla).

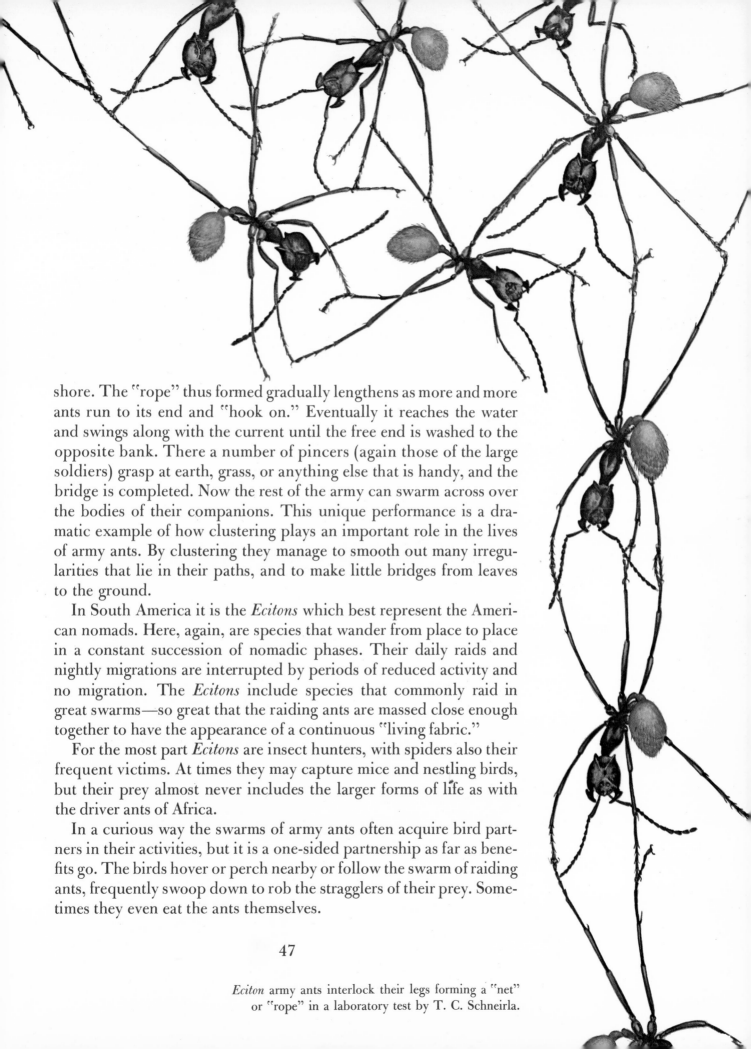

shore. The "rope" thus formed gradually lengthens as more and more ants run to its end and "hook on." Eventually it reaches the water and swings along with the current until the free end is washed to the opposite bank. There a number of pincers (again those of the large soldiers) grasp at earth, grass, or anything else that is handy, and the bridge is completed. Now the rest of the army can swarm across over the bodies of their companions. This unique performance is a dramatic example of how clustering plays an important role in the lives of army ants. By clustering they manage to smooth out many irregularities that lie in their paths, and to make little bridges from leaves to the ground.

In South America it is the *Ecitons* which best represent the American nomads. Here, again, are species that wander from place to place in a constant succession of nomadic phases. Their daily raids and nightly migrations are interrupted by periods of reduced activity and no migration. The *Ecitons* include species that commonly raid in great swarms—so great that the raiding ants are massed close enough together to have the appearance of a continuous "living fabric."

For the most part *Ecitons* are insect hunters, with spiders also their frequent victims. At times they may capture mice and nestling birds, but their prey almost never includes the larger forms of life as with the driver ants of Africa.

In a curious way the swarms of army ants often acquire bird partners in their activities, but it is a one-sided partnership as far as benefits go. The birds hover or perch nearby or follow the swarm of raiding ants, frequently swoop down to rob the stragglers of their prey. Sometimes they even eat the ants themselves.

47

Eciton army ants interlock their legs forming a "net" or "rope" in a laboratory test by T. C. Schneirla.

The Argentine ant (*Iridomyrmex*) is a nomad on a really large scale. For one thing, it has no permanent nest, setting up colonies wherever food is abundant. Fertile queens lose no time in finding newly located colonies and so the range of the species constantly spreads. Though it is named for the land of the Argentine, apparently its original territory was Brazil and Bolivia. After becoming established in Argentina, it became a world traveler. One trip was to New Orleans—probably in a shipment of coffee. From there it soon made its way to Tennessee, North Carolina, Texas, and even to one isolated area in Chicago. Not many years later it was noticed in California. Going still farther afield, the Argentine ant stowed away in fodder that was shipped to Cape Town in Africa, and before long it was all over the southern part of that continent as well as in the Canary Islands. Nor did Europe escape from its invasions. During the past fifty years it has taken over one European country after another.

Wherever the Argentine ant goes, the native ants begin to disappear. The South American nomads take over from their own kind as well as from people! In some areas they are able to live in the open the year around, but where this is impossible they move into houses for the cold seasons. Here they swarm into every kind of food, into clothing and furniture. A hotel in Paris once had to be emptied of its residents because of these unwelcome insects.

Little wonder Argentine ants are so successful if we consider how rapidly they multiply. Always their increase is fantastic; one colony

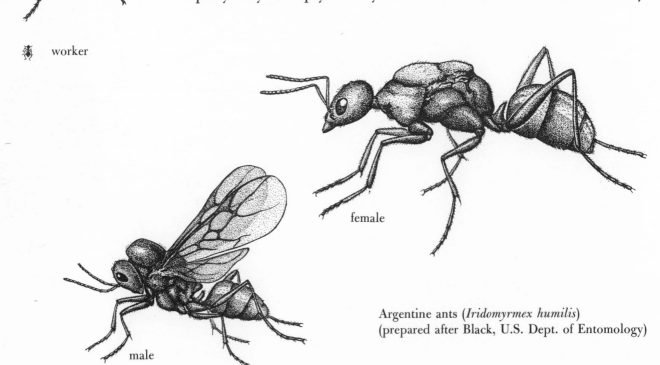

worker

female

male

Argentine ants (*Iridomyrmex humilis*)
(prepared after Black, U.S. Dept. of Entomology)

Opening to ant
nests in the
thorns of an
Acacia

Tiny wax-like bodies on tips
of leaflets, being rich in
oil, are harvested by ants
living in thorns.

under observation grew from one hundred individuals to ten thousand
between spring and fall.

Sometimes the fierce behavior of ants serves to aid something besides themselves. For example, there is an extremely warlike species,
the *Azteca*, which lives in the Cecropia trees of Brazil, often in enor-
mous colonies. Though small in size, they are frightening enough to
keep most other insects away, and the trees benefit as a result. They
swarm out of their large fabricated nests in great numbers at the first
sign of being molested.

Certain Acacia trees in the tropics also have such helpful inhabitants. They bear hollow thorns, which the ants find to be good living
quarters and for which they "defend" the trees. For a long time it was
thought this arrangement was following some kind of natural law—
that the trees and ants were actually dependent upon each other for
survival. However, this theory is now seriously doubted, for observations reveal that the trees can do very well without the ants, and
the ants can thrive in other kinds of settings.

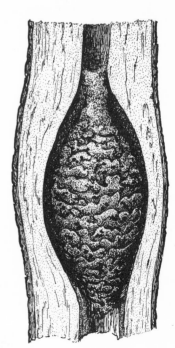

Nest in Cecropia
tree trunk.

49

Cricket attached to a Formica queen feeding on oily secretions from the ant's body.

Tiny wingless cricket (*Myrmecophila nebrascensis*) which often inhabits ant nests.

ANT FRIENDS AND ENEMIES

Through many generations writers have liked to use the ant as a symbol of industry. In such cases it appears as a creature of virtue. But other writings suggest this insect is stingy and selfish—the most noted case being the fable of the grasshopper and the ant. In the ancient tale a grasshopper that has been playing all summer comes, starving, in the winter to beg food of the ant, only to be cruelly refused.

To disprove the logic of this tale, we need only to look at the yearly program of a grasshopper. By the time fall days have ended, adult grasshoppers have no need for food. Their eggs have been laid; through the winter their larvae will lie in protected places awaiting warm weather. Those cheerful individuals which were so lively during the summer have died away; they couldn't possibly go begging at an ant's storehouse.

If we look back to find the origin of this legend, we see it was made famous by the Greek teller of fables, Aesop. However, he apparently had his inspiration from folklore of India, where the Hindus had used a similar animal story to illustrate the wisdom of thrift. But it is believed that, in their version, the animal begging from the ant was not a grasshopper, although it may have been another insect. At any rate, when Aesop told his story, the beggar was a cicada. Many years later two Frenchmen, La Fontaine and Grandville, in story and illustrations gave new life to the tale, and this time the cicada became a grasshopper. So, with complete disregard of natural-history facts, the world was given an image of the gay yet pitiful grasshopper and the industrious but mean-spirited ant.

While this story has no foundation in fact, ants have associations with many other insects, which should indeed inspire storytelling

50

with a ring of truth. Look, for example, at a tiny roach, golden in color, which makes its home in the nests of fungus-growing ants. Its whole way of life is dependent on its hosts: the little roaches continuously lick secretions from the coats of the soldier caste of ants. The secretions provide them with nourishment, and the licking keeps the ants' skin clean. They never leave the ant nests, and because of the countless years they have spent in darkness, they have lost their sight. They are named *Attaphila*, meaning "friend of the *Attas*," for their most notable association is with the *Atta* ants, the fungus growers described on page 41.

For a long time it was a puzzle as to how *Attaphila*, with its lack of sight, managed to find its way to new ant homes. The answer, finally discovered, is that, as the queens-in-the-making are about to leave a nest on a wedding flight, female roaches "stow away" on their backs. When the *Atta* females return to earth, each to start a new colony, there are their little friends with them to continue the same close association.

A tiny beetle that seeks out ants is not so helpful. In fact it robs its hosts, giving nothing in return. Its deception is to take small bits of soil and cover itself except for one little spot over the mouth. Thus camouflaged it backs against the wall of the ant nest and waits quietly. When an ant worker comes along with a newly laid egg, looking for a place to stow it, the tiny opening looks promising. She puts it there, then as she hurries off to tend another one, the beetle extends its jaws—and the egg is consumed. And the opening again remains waiting for another trusting nurse to come along.

Another beetle that makes its home with ants, but which may be said to "play fair," is the clavigerid. Even though the clavigerid beetles are blind they are able to seek out the ants and beg for food with gestures typical of an ant. The ants obligingly spit up drops of food for them. In return the beetles have no objection to the ants licking a sweet liquid that is secreted from clumps of hair growing on their backs. Here is real cooperation!

Still another beetle, *Lomachusa*, while giving the appearance of being an ant friend, in reality is a foe and a serious threat to any colony to which it is attached. Like the clavigerid beetle, it secretes a liquid from its hair, and this is relished by the ants. But apparently it is not a food so much as a drug, and the ants become addicted to it to such an extent that they ignore the harm the beetles are doing their colony. Slavishly they care for the beetles and their larvae, even though these larvae are eating their own brood. If it were not for a mistaken notion

Two views of the golden roach (*Attaphila fungicola*) found in the fungus gardens of Atta texana. (Prepared after Wheeler)

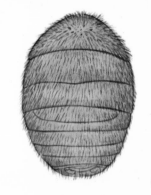

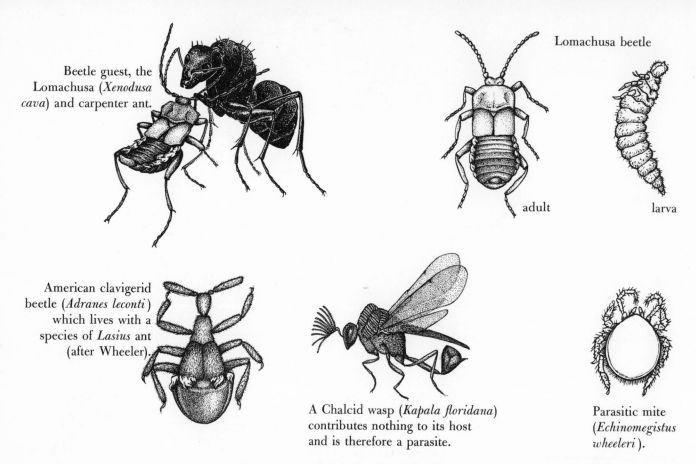

Beetle guest, the Lomachusa (*Xenodusa cava*) and carpenter ant.

Lomachusa beetle

adult

larva

American clavigerid beetle (*Adranes leconti*) which lives with a species of *Lasius* ant (after Wheeler).

A Chalcid wasp (*Kapala floridana*) contributes nothing to its host and is therefore a parasite.

Parasitic mite (*Echinomegistus wheeleri*).

on the part of the ants, the colony would be doomed by the *Lomachusa* in their midst. The mistake occurs when the beetle larvae have grown and are ready to pupate. The ants then treat them as they do their own larvae, burying each one in a little hollow in the earth. Unfortunately for the beetle's future, the cocoon which covers a larva is delicate—far more so than the cocoon of an ant larva—and as the ant worker moves the little bundle, the silk is damaged. The ant will notice this; something is wrong! So she pulls out the larva and buries it again. At this the beetle larva automatically starts spinning a new cocoon, and the effort of the repeat performance is too much. It cannot pupate. The result of all this is that the only *Lomachusa* larvae which have a chance of survival are those which the ants overlook. Only an occasional ant colony is destroyed by its self-invited guests, the *Lomachusa*.

Altogether it has been estimated that about five thousand different kinds of creatures are attached to ant colonies. Careful investigation of almost any nest is quite sure to reveal one or several of these "hangers-on," which may have moved in by accident, or may have sought out the ants or been "invited" by them. Among the uninvited guests often are caterpillars, grubs, worms, wood lice, and various insect larvae. Some of these intruders, once discovered by the ants, are attacked and defeated by them; but again, their defenses are too

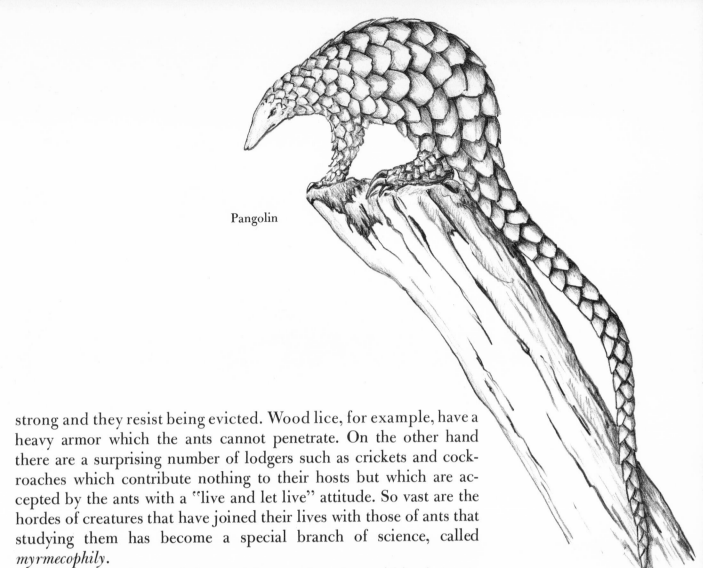

Pangolin

strong and they resist being evicted. Wood lice, for example, have a heavy armor which the ants cannot penetrate. On the other hand there are a surprising number of lodgers such as crickets and cockroaches which contribute nothing to their hosts but which are accepted by the ants with a "live and let live" attitude. So vast are the hordes of creatures that have joined their lives with those of ants that studying them has become a special branch of science, called *myrmecophily*.

Ant enemies that work from without rather than within the nests are not so numerous as might be expected, for in general ants are not considered tasty fare. However, some spiders do prey upon them and so do a variety of reptiles and mammals. In some parts of the world they are eaten even by people. Among the mammals, the most notable ant eater is known by just that name—anteater, although sometimes it is called the ant bear. Another mammal concentrating on the same

Aardvark

diet is the pangolin, or scaly anteater. An armored beast called the armadillo is particularly fond of ants and termites; so also is the odd character named aardvark.

The anteaters (there are three different kinds) all are native to tropical America. A long-drawn-out head makes them easy to recognize. Inside the long, long jaws is a wormlike tongue capable of being extended quickly to a considerable distance. Although it has no teeth, strong claws on the front feet equip the animal for tearing into the nests of ants and termites, and the tongue scoops the insects into the mouth in countless numbers. (In captivity anteaters are given a vegetable diet.) The pangolin, looking as much like an overgrown spruce cone as an animal, has a shorter face, but its sticky tongue can be extended a number of inches beyond its mouth, capturing quantities of insects in one thrust. Several different kinds of pangolins range over the Far East and much of southern Africa. Aardvarks also belong to Africa. They differ from other ant eaters in having teeth, but they, too, have a long, sticky tongue which is principally used for gathering up ants and termites.

It is the fate of ants to have attracted one of the strangest of all animal enemies—a small creature that seems devoted to the single action of trapping them. Because of the way it accomplishes this result, it has been christened "ant lion." Actually it is the larva of a winged, night-flying dragon fly.

Armadillo

The Ant Lion (*Myrmeleon immaculatus*)

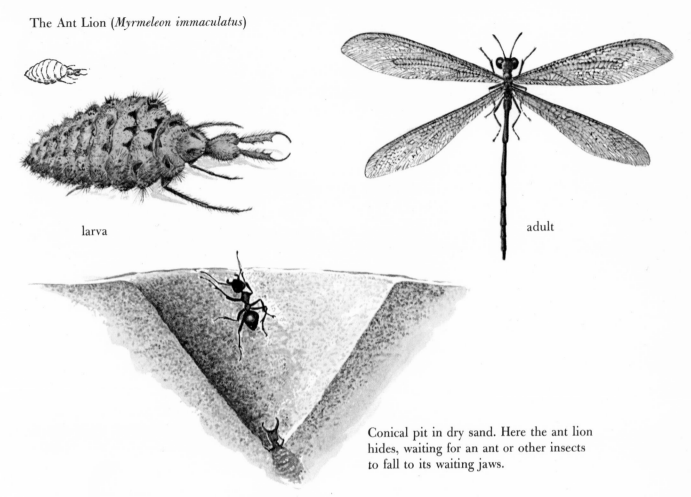

larva

adult

Conical pit in dry sand. Here the ant lion hides, waiting for an ant or other insects to fall to its waiting jaws.

When the larva develops from egg stage, it has short, feeble legs which cannot carry it in search of food, but it does have a useful, square flat head and sharply pointed jaws. With the head it flips up dirt and begins to plow into the earth, making a circle. When the first circle is completed, a second trench just inside is dug, the ant lion scooping dirt onto its head, then flipping it up and out. Work is continued until a funnel-shaped pit about two inches deep and three inches across has been completed. Now the ant lion buries itself at the bottom of the excavation, completely hidden except for its jaws. As the ants in the neighborhood go about their various tasks, many of them stop to have a look into the "something new" that has appeared in their midst. The trap is then sprung as loose soil at the edge of the pit gives way and the inquisitive ant standing there begins to slip. To help things along the ant lion flips up some dirt which falls in a shower on its victim—and quickly the ant is within the jaws of the little trapper.

55

A termite mound in Australia

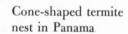

Cone-shaped termite
nest in Panama

Mushroom-shaped nest of African
termites 3 to 6 inches high

THE TERMITE STORY

It is true that people all over the world are likely to call termites "white ants" even though they are not ants and often are not white. Actually termites and ants are so different and distinct from each other that science places them in two different orders. The ants belong to Hymenoptera ("membrane wings"); the termites belong to Isoptera ("equal wings"). This is one distinction for anyone who happens to see these insects in their winged form to look for: the ant's two pairs of wings are of different lengths, while those of the termite are the same. Termite wings, also, are large—usually twice the length of the body—while an ant's wings are never more than body length.

The body forms vary too—the ant's having a pinched-in "waist" between thorax and abdomen, while the termite is not indented. A termite larva has six legs as the adult does, while the larva of an ant has none.

Another outstanding difference between termites and ants (and most other insects, for that matter) is that they have kept a place in their society for males. Where the male ants mate with the queens-to-be, then quickly die, in the termite society the male joins his mate in starting a colony. As workers develop and building gets under way, a large apartment is constructed, which the royal couple will occupy for five or more years. It must be roomy, for the queen grows to a length of four or five inches, and her abdomen becomes greatly distended with eggs so that it looks like a fat, greasy cylinder. The queen is then unable to move about under her own power. She does not need to, for hundreds of workers, working in relays, constantly stuff food into her little mouth. Other workers keep busy licking her sides clean while still others

56

carry away the eggs that she lays in fantastic numbers. With some species a single queen may produce many thousands of eggs every day. In the course of her "reign" she may become the mother of millions! Meanwhile the king is well fed and cared for also. His single duty is to fertilize the eggs.

Altogether, even though the ants and termites have social organizations and many habits that are quite similar, each deserves its own niche in the animal kingdom. The Swedish botanist Linnaeus is responsible for the termite's name. He chose it because of a mistaken idea, confusing the termite with the "death-watch beetle," and bestowing a name that means "the end of life" for that reason.

Termites appeared on earth millions of years ago, at about the time dinosaurs were dying away. Studies of fossil impressions give evidence that their ancestors were closely related to roaches—apparently the oldest of all insects in the world. In those ancient days the termites would not have seemed to be well equipped for survival: they had no armor, were small and soft, and were not able to stand sunlight. Originally they carried no stinger or poison to protect themselves against enemies. Nevertheless they not only survived but increased their kind to fantastic numbers.

How did they do it? One weapon they developed was a special gland on the heads of the soldiers. With some species a liquid can be squirted from this which evaporates to form a poisonous gas. With other species it is a sticky secretion. Either of these when shot at ants (chief foe of the termites) may confuse and turn them away, or actually entangle them.

To avoid the sunlight, which is deadly to them, the termites take darkness along with them by building tunnels whenever they leave their nests, although some use the easier method of foraging for food at night or making only short, quick trips from the nest. Their building activities include the construction of remarkably efficient nests, with mounds sloped so that water is drained off them promptly and built-in tubes and spires to provide ventilation and moisture control. In South Africa the interior of a termite home, on a blistering day when the outside of the mound was too hot to touch, proved to have a temperature of only eighty-six. Termites, it seems, worked out air-conditioning systems long before man's inventions in this field.

It is in the tropics that termites have their greatest development, both in activity and in numbers of species, for the continuous warmth there favors them. Some of the greatest colonies are in Africa, while many thrive in South America, Australia, and

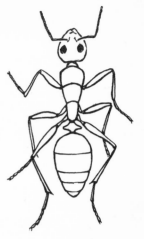

ant worker
note pinched-in "waist"

termite worker
note broad "waist"

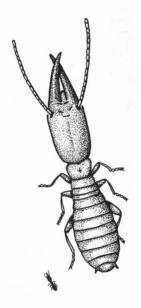

termite soldier

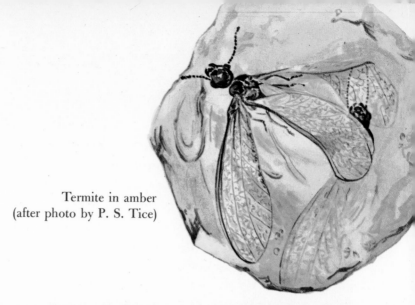

Termite in amber
(after photo by P. S. Tice)

winged adult

Panama. There are species, however, that flourish all too well (from man's point of view) in temperate regions. They are in every state of our country and in parts of Canada, although by far the greatest number of species is found near the Mexican border and the Gulf of Mexico.

While some termites live inside the trunks and branches of dead trees, others go underground to construct elaborate homes with living rooms, storerooms, and nurseries. These are covered with great mounds in which there are more rooms and passageways. Some species make a home on the outside of a living tree, chewing wood pulp to plaster over the bark, thus forming both a nest and endless covered passageways. The termitaries (as the great tropical termite mounds are called) may be as high as twenty feet and several feet square. Most often they are made of sand grains cemented together, and they become so hard they resist breaking by ax or crowbar. There is no end to the shapes they make take, although umbrella-top or mushroom forms are very popular.

A great many termites have need of moisture in the soil, but it seems there are all types to flourish in every kind of situation. For instance there is the "powder-post" termite which lives in dry, sound wood and has no contact whatever with soil. Other species thrive in rotten wood and in wood that is merely damp. On our own continent those that live underground are more numerous than the above-ground species, and those that make their nests in wood fortunately are not so widespread as the inhabitants of the soil, but there are still enough to cause considerable damage. Not only house structures of wood, but furniture and other wooden products, as well as cloth, are ruined by them. They are responsible for many millions of dollars worth of damage every year in spite of endless work to keep them under control. But before we judge termites as being entirely vicious troublemakers, we should realize that there are ways in which they are beneficial from man's stand-·

point. For example, in forests fallen trees might begin to clog vegetation if it were not for the never-ending consumption of wood by these insects. However, even in forests they may be destroyers, as they kill living trees which then become suitable for their own uses.

The fact that termites actually eat wood is one of the oddest facts about them. What a strange diet! How can anything derive nourishment from it since dry wood is composed of cellulose—and neither beasts, birds, nor insects (including termites) can digest it. However, living in the body of every adult worker termite are some tiny organisms known as Protozoa, and they *can* digest cellulose. As a termite chews and swallows wood, the Protozoa take it in and live on it. A whole colony of them is in each termite's body, with some always dying. It is these corpses which actually nourish the termite with "predigested" wood.

Food other than wood must be obtained by the worker termites for their queen, king, and young. To produce it, some species make their own gardens in which grow tiny mushrooms. This is much in the manner of mushroom-growing ants, with one interesting difference. The termites exist in such numbers (possibly having millions in one colony) that enough mushrooms could not possibly be raised for all, and the workers which tend the gardens and carry food to the royal couple and the babies never get to eat the mushrooms themselves. But again we find life making a complete circle: when a queen dies, her body is devoured by her "subjects," thus furnishing nourishment for the future of the colony.

In very large termite colonies there may be several royal couples. There are also the soldiers with oddly shaped heads, having huge jaws that can be used like a scythe. A head may serve, among other things, to plug a break in the nest until workers can repair it. The termite workers are soft, flabby, and blind; it is little wonder they are timid. But what they lack in courage they make up for in industry. Observations have revealed that the workers never rest, but keep on their jobs night and day.

Here, then, are strong bonds that termites and ants have in common: the instinct for social living and organization, untiring industry, and an ability to survive under almost any kind of circumstances. Other insects may be more attractive to man, or more beneficial, but none is more interesting. The extraordinary success of ants and termites for survival on planet Earth surely makes them deserving of our close attention.

male termite

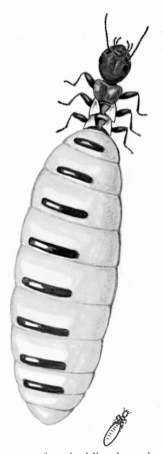

queen after shedding her wings

INDEX

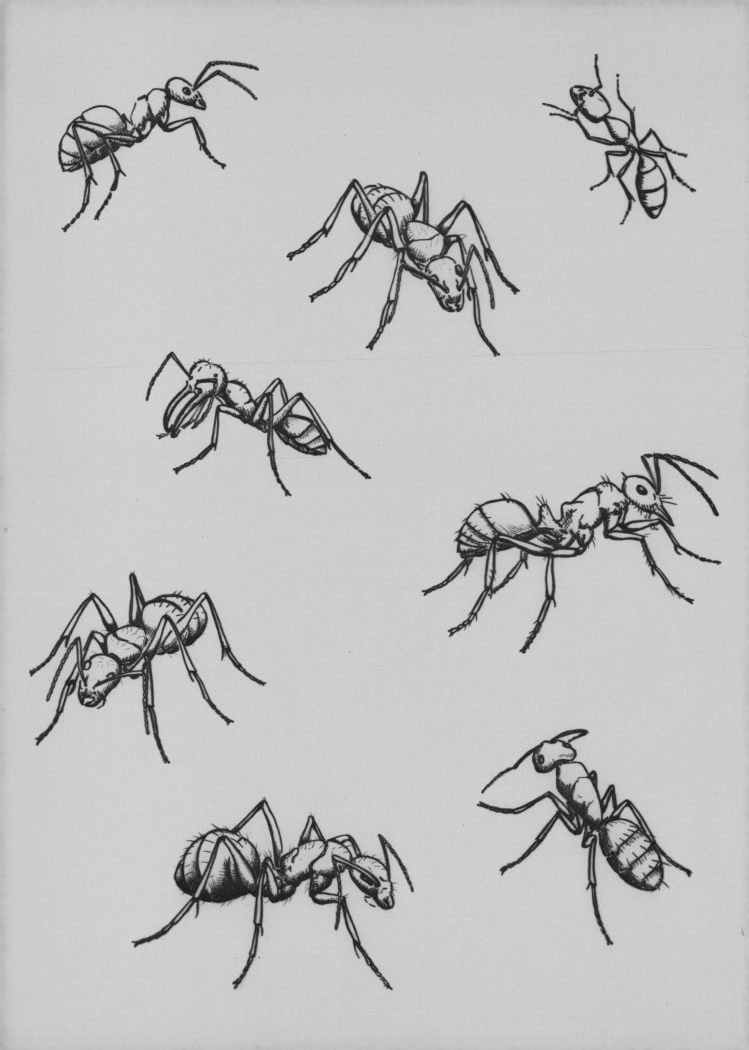

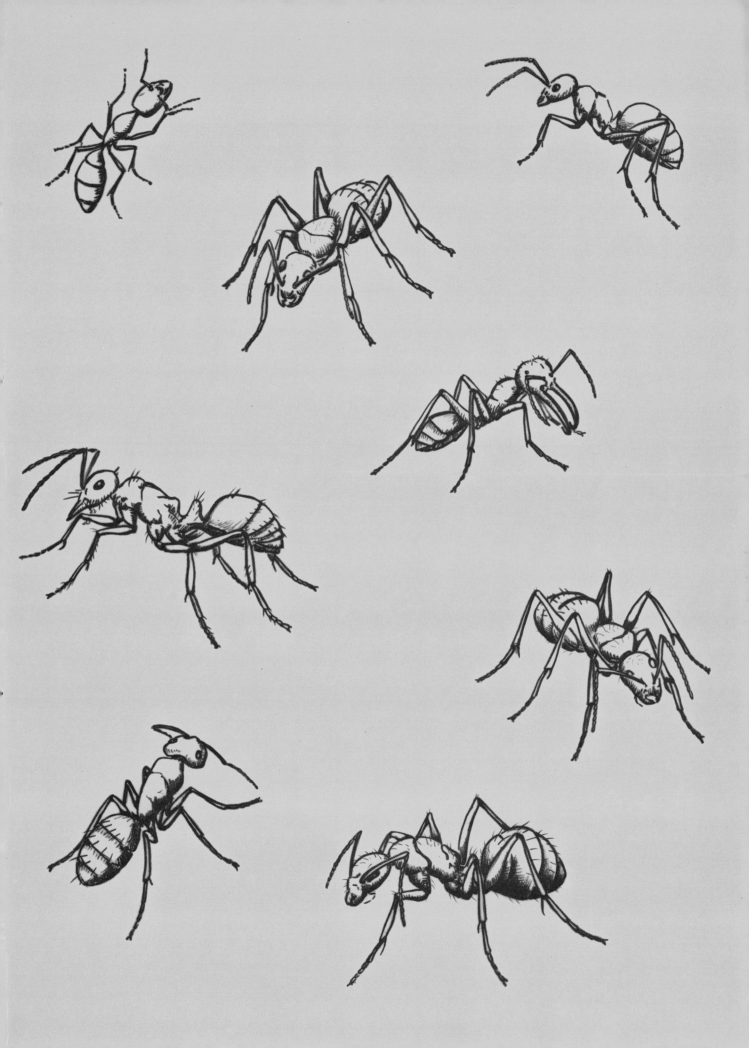